# Spirit Herbs

## Native American Healing

*Mary Dean Atwood*

Sterling Publishing Co., Inc   New York

**Also by Mary Dean Atwood**
Spirit Healing: Native American Magic & Medicine

Library of Congress Cataloging-in-Publication Data Available

10  9  8  7  6  5  4  3  2  1

Published by Sterling Publishing Company, Inc.
387 Park Avenue South, New York, N.Y. 10016
© 1998 by Mary Dean Atwood
Distributed in Canada by Sterling Publishing
℅ Canadian Manda Group, One Atlantic Avenue, Suite 105
Toronto, Ontario, Canada M6K 3E7
Distributed in Great Britain and Europe by Cassell PLC
Wellington House, 125 Strand, London WC2R 0BB, England
Distributed in Australia by Capricorn Link (Australia) Pty Ltd.
P.O. Box 6651, Baulkham Hills, Business Centre, NSW 2153, Australia
Manufactured in the United States of America

Sterling  ISBN 0-8069-3862-5

*This book is dedicated
to all my teachers and students
past, present and future,
wherever they are.*

# Acknowledgments

I wish to thank Sheila Anne Barry and all the staff at Sterling Publishing for having the foresight to recognize that medicine, in whatever form, recognizes truth and will continue to do so. I welcome this opportunity to teach and share my knowledge as researched and experienced.

My appreciation to Deborah Wareing and Michael Campbell who contributed their computer expertise and to others offering help and inspiration.

# Contents

# Introduction

When the European settlers arrived on the continent of North America, they found Native Americans healthy and robust. Smallpox, tuberculosis, bubonic plague, syphilis and other horrible diseases were unknown to the Indians. Early white settlers believed bathing abominable and used no soap. They considered native customs, such as bathing, sweating and fasting, barbaric.

For centuries religious settlers were frightened by the chanting and rattling of charms, animal totems, the burning of herbs, and the use of song and prayer to cure illness. Cries of witchcraft and constant persecution eradicated those immigrants who contributed to folk healing. In addition, the pilgrims had little knowledge of the plants and environment they encountered to help them.

The Native American medicine healers actually were advanced in their holistic approach to healing. Methods used included assessment of personal problems, family or tribal intervention, and client dream interpretation to uncover hidden needs and fears. Shamans burned sacred herbs, called for help from powerful spirit guides and dispensed necessary energy through their hands, totems, or prayers. For serious physical problems or community conflicts, the whole family or tribe gathered together to be included in the healing process. Secret medicine societies of respected elders met together to solve problems affecting the tribe.

In addition to physical illness or damage by accidents or battles, misfortunes occurred when anger or undesirable energy forces attacked a tribal member. Sometimes a person offended a nature or animal spirit, forgetting to show proper reverence and respect. Perhaps a jealous shaman or enemy cast a spell and sickness resulted. Negative feelings or other undesirable attitudes of the client caused illness.

Interestingly, the Native American healer recognized the potential dangers of the unconscious wishes and needs of the individual when denied expression. These concerns fascinated the white settlers because they made little connection between the mind and the health of the body. Unfortunately, in many modern health clinics, *mental state and environment are still ignored!* One might ask which medicine, old or new, is the most primitive?

Medicine healers looked into the unseen world of the body—the thoughts or dreams of the patient—to deduce the cause of sickness. There the offending spirit or personal problem was located. Sometimes the medicine man or woman left the earth and traveled to the land of the ancestors to obtain necessary information. Their prophecies, often for the benefit of the tribe, came from powerful guides.

The medicine doctors brought their pouches of marvelous totems, songs, prayers and gifts to incur spirit cooperation and enhance curative powers. Specific healing techniques often included the use of plants or herbs. Rituals included the offerings of sacred herbs such as sage and tobacco.

Lack of knowledge of chemical properties of herbs didn't lessen the medicine man or woman's effectiveness. If an object appeared to cause pleasant or healing events, it was good medicine.

If a plant or totem had medicine, it had power. Trial and error, undoubtedly, contributed to the acquired knowledge. Modern analyses of the chemical composition of plants document the healing qualities of herbs used by the Indians. Today, natural herbal and synthetic duplication of compounds account for numerous over-the-counter and prescriptive medicines.

Observations of early white settlers noted remedies worked faster and with better results on Native Americans than on the settlers. Reasons believed to influence outcome were better physical condition of the Indian and magical or "devilish" practices of the medicine healer.

When the colonies desired independence from England, they recognized the need for local pharmaceutical supplies and knowledge of indigenous plants and herbs. Unfortunately, thousands of Native Americans already had died of diseases brought from the continent, since they had no natural antibodies to previously nonexistent germs and bacteria. Shamans were dead or dishonored, and those who were left loathed giving away their secrets, believing the rituals lost power when disclosed.

White religious leaders viewed healers as obstacles to converting natives to Christianity. Government officials feared Indian leaders' influence in preventing confiscation of their territory. Consequently, invaluable medicinal practices known to the Indians were rejected or lost.

Now, five hundred years after the pilgrims' arrival, research studies reveal that more people seek alternative health practitioners using natural remedies, holistic approaches or spiritual methods than visit standard medical doctors. The percentage continues to grow as awareness increases in healing from the use of nature's bounty and energies not always explained by known physical laws.

We wish to know more about the ways of the medicine men and women who recognized these forces. As the Grandmothers and Grandfathers watch us from the Path of Souls, they, no doubt, are pleased with the wonders of modern medical science. Perhaps they wish for a combined joint effort of old and new to heal ourselves and our planet. We only hope the Native American ancestors who guide our knowledge and wisdom show us the patience and honor not accorded them.

> The Crows and Minnetares have religious ceremonies regularly at the new and full moon throughout the year. The medicine men are looked to secure favorable weather, the health of the people, good crops, the growth of the grass, the safe birth of children.... They perform their religious ceremonies for the people free of charge. —*Lewis Henry Morgan 1862*[1]

> The medicine of the Indian is a misnomer. It means a religious ceremony or an act of worship. Nothing more, nothing less, accompanied when performed for sick persons with such forms as to show the extent of the superstition which penetrates their faith and worship. —*Lewis Henry Morgan 1862*[2]

> What treasures of medicine may not be expected from a people, who although destitute of the lights of science, have discovered the properties of some of the most inestimable medicines. —*Dr. Benjamin Barton 1798*[3]

> God continues to be served here, in spite of the opposition of the devil. In public they perform a hundred mummeries full of impiety; and talk to the skins of animals, and to dead birds, as divinities. *They claim that medicinal herbs are gods, from whom they have life,* and that no others be worshipped. Every day they sing songs in honor of their little manitous, as they call them. They inveigh against our religion and against the missionaries. —*Father Julien Binneteau 1699*[4]

> A drunken man who had fallen into a fire was burnt in such a manner.... I did not think he could recover; yet they cured him in ten Days, so that he went about. I knew another blown up with Powder that was cured to Admiration. I never saw an Indian have an Ulcer, or foul Wound in my life; neither is there any such thing to be found among them. —*John Lawson 1714*[5]

# 1 Medicine and Power

*Wakan Tanka as Grandfather is the Great Spirit independent of manifestation, unqualified, unlimited, identical to the Christian Godhead or to the Hindu Brahma-Nirguna. Wakan-Takan as Father is the Great Spirit considered in relation to His manifestation, either as Creator, Preserver, or Destroyer, identical to the Christian God, or to the Hindu Brahma-Saguna...the Earth is considered under two aspects, that of Mother and Grandmother. The former is the earth considered as the producer of all growing forms, in act; whereas Grandmother refers to the ground or substance of all growing things—potentiality.* [6]

## Cosmology

The American Indians had a rich cosmological mythology. Students of Native American religion believe the term *mythology* is misleading due to similarities in traditional sacred beliefs with those of other major religions of the world including Christianity. Although authorities disagree, Indian tribes conceived a central power source translated in English as the Great Spirit. This divine spiritual essence, shaped and evolved the universe into form.

In dispute is whether the different spirit forms are the One Power in varying representations as opposed to an army of distinctly separate lesser spirits much like the Christian angels. Wak Ka Tah, Wakan, Wakan Tanka, or Wakonda, names for the Great Spirit in different Indian languages, is the conceptualization of God as a vast universal power. The question is whether it is a deity with the ability to manifest itself in different forms or a single, powerful energy or entity ruling over the direction of lesser spirit helpers in animal, nature, or humanlike form. We will never know the original Native American concept of the Great Spirit due to four hundred years of their living among missionaries. Other ancient religions considered God to manifest in various forms as well as to be formless and invisible. One thing is certain, the Native American conceptualization of God was not limited to a human, manlike image.

Native Americans believed powerful spirits created and shaped the world. In Indian mythology, supernatural creators of the world were a divine energy. The divine essences, such as animal or nature beings, shifted at will from one form to another, to heal, to teach lessons, or to mold the heavens. These shape-shifting beings always were considered to be in spirit form, not actual animals or climatic conditions.

Native Americans believed power could reside in any natural object. All living things had life both visible and invisible. Plants were part of the same kingdom as people. Both shared a consciousness and had power. Any natural object, animate or inanimate, had an essence which could be described as a soul or life force.

Other great religions emphasize the concept that all substances from the earth originated and developed from a universal life force. The Greek, Anaxagoras, designated the Nous or the animating Soul as present in every atom. Helena P. Blavatasky, author of *The Secret Doctrine*, noted "the conception of a general Spirit-Soul pervading all Nature is the oldest of all philosophical notions."

Native Americans didn't see the world in hierarchical fashion, with the spirits ranked from the highest to the lowest according to a power structure. However, the One God or Great Spirit was generally considered unavailable for assisting in mundane earthly affairs. Semidivine spirits such as Corn Maiden and Rain Maker existed to respond to prayers for help from those on earth.

The Navajo are an exception. According to Harold Driver, author of *Indians of North America*, the Navajo believed the dominant leader of the world creators to be Changing Woman. She created humans and helped teach them how to control the forces of nature. "Second in importance to Changing Woman is her husband the Sun.... Third in rank are the Hero Twins, Monster Slayer and Child of the Water.... Of lesser importance are First Man and First Woman. First Man was creator of the universe." There were several groups of lesser spirits, which included Coyote and Thunder People.

Changing Woman was the only holy personality that was always helpful to humans. All the others switched at will into fearful creatures such as tricksters or witches.

## Mysterious Medicine

The word *medicine* in the Native American sense means a movement of energy with effects not explained except by the supernatural or mysterious. Medicine is invisible and intangible, the Indians' conception of the one force animating all life.

Power, or medicine, results from receiving favor and strength from the Great Spirit, whose energy extends to plants, animals and nature beings. These spirit helpers let the Indians "borrow" attributes in time of need and granted wishes—like the Christian angelic forces that perform miracles to help people on earth. Surveys show eighty percent of Americans believe in the existence of angels.

To the Native Americans, health, food, and survival depended on higher powers, like the animal and plant beings, to provide crops, survival skills and, sometimes, life itself. Through prayer, ritual, reference and ceremony to The Being, or Beings, the Native Americans asked to become one with the spirit, to acquire the spirit's characteristics for themselves. This gave them power. If you had "medicine" you had power.

Healing with herbs was only one way cures were achieved. Generally healing granted by spirits ranked above physical cures, although physical cures helped. Today we know the spiritual/mental/emotional dimension is as important to healing as are physical medicines. For this reason the author will use history and a story to demonstrate the historical Indian conception of "medicine" and follow with suggestions for building your power base, including the use of power herbs.

## MEDICINE DOGS

Horses, as powerful representatives of animal beings, were called "medicine dogs." Like the native dog, they were helpers and carriers for man, but possessed unusual strength. The animals, which arrived in America on European ships, seemed magical as they carried man at great speeds for long distances.

Horses, like the white man, appeared suddenly when Cortez and his Spanish soldiers arrived to conquer the Aztecs. To the Native American, no white man or horse existed before that event in 1519. The Indians saw the horse as an incredible creature. As horses became more numerous, Indians used them to hunt food sources and chase enemies.

The white man, with his strange dress and "medicine dogs," gave the illusion of mighty beings. Savvy historians recognize the importance of the appearance of the horse in the overthrow of Montezuma, whose forces greatly outnumbered the Spanish explorers. Unfortunately for the red man, before Cortez landed the Aztec king Montezuma had dreamed of the arrival of a god and offered little resistance.

While the greedy behavior of the Europeans was hardly Godlike, the prophet Montezuma correctly dreamed that the future of his people would forever be changed by the influx of individuals from different continents and with alien customs.

Totems represented the nature or characteristic of the animal or spirit being which had power. Because of the usefulness and strength of the horse, horse totems as symbols for the animal were common. With these, the energy of the horse was harnessed and good luck resulted.

## An Indian Story of Power

Runs Too Fast, a Dakota Sioux brave, considered himself lucky. Sitting Bull, his chief, guided the tribe in defending pride and honor against their enemies. His tribe feasted on all the buffalo they could eat, his pony fattened from all the tall grass surrounding the tribe's Rosebud village in the Dakotas. As he watched his horse, Powder Dog, munch on sweet grass, Runs Too Fast remembered first seeing him during a raid on an enemy tribe to the northwest.

During the previous winter, Crow warriors stole many of their horses, killing one Sioux brave, Leg Knows River, as he tried to stop them. Sitting Bull declared a war party should recover the losses and if possible add additional horses. Because Runs Too Fast passed this test of bravery, the war council now included him in the Big Horse Society made up of village warriors who counted coup.

As Runs Too Fast and his fellow clansmen approached the Crow camp, the black and white mustang was the first of the ponies to whinny. Immediately after spotting Powder Dog he felt he must claim this horse as his own. The moonlight seemed to illuminate the white spots on his coat. The reflection off the spots appeared to dance alone as the pony's black horsehair was almost invisible. It was as if the moon reached down to point out this horse with the dancing spots, perhaps a gift from the Moon Being.

The young warrior connected a rope to the Crow horse gear already between his teeth. Runs Too Fast noted Powder Dog easily followed the lead of his new rider. Even though it was the Moon Of The Cherries and plants had barely started to sprout after a hard winter, Powder Dog's coat rippled in the moonlight, showing a fine, muscular structure. The minute he mounted his new "medicine dog," Runs Too Fast knew the Great Spirit had helped him to become a great warrior. Now powerful medicine accompanied him on his hunts and battles. The capture of Powder Dog, a trained horse in an enemy camp, counted as his first coup. This act of bravery gave him the right to wear the first eagle feather in his hair.

Again the memory of the Crow foot raid entered his mind. He wasn't so brave as he prepared for his first raid on an enemy tribe. He remembered the pounding of fear in his chest. What if he failed to prove himself as a powerful warrior and disgraced himself and his relatives?

He prepared his war medicine bag carefully. His mother fashioned a small leather pouch, which fit over his shoulder and right under his armpit, hugging his body. He fashioned the symbol of the Bear Clan to which they belonged on the overlapping flap. In the pouch he carefully placed a tiny crystal for spirit direction, a pinch of tobacco for spirit favor, a small metal casing from the end of a bullet bought from traders for fighting skill, and a bead from a dead Crow's hair to ensure their defeat.

The top of the strap fastened to his necklace of bone and beads, which he prepared before the raid. One round piece of horse leg bone strung through the natural hole in the middle surrounded small bones of fierce animal fighters like badger and cougar and feathers of hawk and eagle. The beads of six colors represented the four directions, the ancestors above, and the earth below.

Quickly strapping his bag full of arrows over his left shoulder, he hurried to join the other warriors.

During the ensuing whooping and fighting, the young warrior froze when two Crow braves both charged him at once from different directions. Without thought and operating on natural instinct he swerved Powder Dog to the right and headed toward the enemy Crow racing toward him. The enemy warrior aimed his arrow at Runs Too Fast and at that exact moment Powder Dog swerved slightly, which caused the arrow to whistle by his ear.

Runs Too Fast quickly took the opportunity to reverse directions and plant his arrow in the charging Crow, knocking the enemy warrior from his horse. The Crow warrior attacking from the other direction, shocked at the failure of his comrade, rode off to find another enemy target. Another Sioux brave galloped over the fallen Crow, but Runs Too Fast, the youngest brave, got to count coup because of his demonstrated fearlessness.

The Dakota Sioux warriors returned to the village with their recaptured horses and some additional Crow mounts. Horses wounded in battle were treated with herbal remedies and decorated with feathers and paint. War horses participated in the Big Horse Dance Ceremony and ate favored grasses. Village warriors saved long strands of horse hair from the manes and tails of horses that helped count coup. Horse hair braided into war implements and bonnets added power, strength and speed to the braves' hunts and battles. Hawk feathers tied to the horses' gear added safety in flight and a keen, watchful eye.

Later, during the Moon Of Making Fat, a Thunderhorse ceremony was performed on a Dakota brave, considered to have contacted "evil medicine" from an enemy Crow during the skirmish. A sacred staff blessed by the spirits was tied to a riderless horse that had survived numerous battles and was thought protected by Eagle Cloud, a powerful being with great speed and wisdom. The horse was painted with red and yellow stripes from his shoulders to his hooves. When the medicine man yelled, the horse galloped out of the village and when the horse returned, the bad spell was over.

Sitting Bull and other important tribal men counted the horses they owned as symbols of their wealth and power. One day, he, Runs Too Fast, would own a dozen horses and have several wives. He hoped he could give wise counsel as an elder like his beloved chief. His horse, Powder Dog, would be buried with him to provide a mount in the afterworld.

Runs Too Fast had no way of knowing that very soon all the Dakota braves and their horses would be needed to fight the encroaching enemy known as the "white eyes."

## Finding Your Power Totem

Olympic winners, medicine healers, politicians, and metaphysical people share one thing in common: they often believe in an object, or "totem," they carry with them to help assure success when competing, healing or needing assistance. Believing in a totem "helper" gives them the self-confidence which makes the difference between success and failure.

The traditional red man uses objects of nature. An Olympic champion might wear the same pair of socks in each competition. A priest places his St. Christopher's medal, or Christian cross, around his neck. A politician uses campaign buttons and slogans as a power affirmation. Single, dating adults hope a special cologne or style of dress will enhance their desirability.

A totem can be any object, hobby, interest, slogan, picture, scent, plant, animal, stone, thought, role model, or song. It should be a positive thought reminder which actually makes you feel good about yourself, increases self-confidence and empowers you. Ideas for finding one will be offered. You don't need more than one but can have as many as you want—provided you focus on a single quality you want to cultivate.

## Magic Inventory

An object or idea for a totem to be your lucky charm is around you. Pretend you are an observing stranger in your surroundings. What indications are present?

1. Do you notice a large number of pictures or art with one theme or subject matter that suggests a totem? An example might be a collection of books or artwork on one subject.
2. Do you have a special hobby or collect ceramic animal statues or other types of figurines?
3. Is there a list of dates for events or activities you wanted to do but never took the time? What do they have in common?
4. Have you purchased information on planting or growing particular flowers or herbs? Do you like certain tastes and smells which remind you of pleasant foods or experiences like hiking or camping?
5. Is there a certain book you've wanted to read on self-improvement or a better quality of life? Are you intrigued by a particular religion or practice like meditation or yoga or representative artifact?
6. A totem can also be a religious figure from your spiritual belief system, e.g., Jesus or Buddha. It can be a symbol such

as a cross, which is widely used as a source of strength and comfort.

7. Have you bought or inherited a special piece of jewelry? Do you have a rock collection (remember, stones have vibrations)?

8. Did someone recently give you a gift that might have special significance, such as a tie or belt with an emblem on it? Do the clothes in your closet have the same color as decorative items in your home?

9. Have you joined an association or studied a particular animal or bird or been interested in preservation of our planet? This could be an important clue to a certain totem.

10. Do you have an interest in astrology or astronomy? Do you have shapes of moons, stars, the sun or other sun sign emblems (like fish for the sun sign Pisces) decorating your home?

Look around your house for an object or idea which might be your totem or lucky charm. Unconsciously, we often have an affinity for items or know what will help us to get in touch with our innermost feelings. Search for the object or an information source to find it and begin immediately to use it. Associate the article with power and self-confidence.

If you can't find any clues, visiting your favorite hobby store, or reading books can help you. The right book appears frequently at a time we need the help it offers; or sometimes a person just happens to bring by a gift at a seemingly coincidental time.

If your lucky charm does not bring you results or renewed confidence, put it away and look again. If you sincerely want your power totem, it will appear in an amazingly timely fashion.

Look for repetitions. One person discovered turtle artifacts all over the house—tape holders, incense burners, jewelry designs and boxes, and stone statues made of jade and soap-stone—combined with a habit of rescuing tortoises and turtles on the highways! All of this when no awareness that any interest in the ancient reptiles existed!

## CARE AND FEEDING OF YOUR TOTEM

First, you must believe in it for it to work. Faith brings joy and optimism, which in turn raises your level of vibrations to a stronger (or higher), more accessible level. The unseen world of angels and spirit guides (or laws of quantum physics if you prefer) operates along powerful energy lines determined by forces we currently are only beginning to discover scientifically. Spiritual people believe a thought is a prayer and what you think is what you create. This belief is the secret behind why a totem works.

Research has shown that the presence of an experimenter and how the equipment is arranged may affect the outcome of the data. Atomic particles so tiny that they cannot be seen under the most powerful microscope can only be measured by the trails they leave behind. Scientific experiments show tiny particles not only have a strange way of behaving the way the experimenter desiresd, but they appear to have a choice whether they are going to act like a wave or a particle!

Experimental research shows that smiling, even when you don't feel like it, actually begins to change blood chemistry and improves the immune system!

The increase in your optimism and consequent higher vibrations are then absorbed by your totem and other items around you. These imbedded vibrations are why psychics can pick up information from holding a person's ring or article of clothing. Their existence is also a good reason to avoid old heirlooms which have a history of bad luck.

There are other practices you can adopt to increase the power of your totem:

1. Keep it wrapped in natural cloth in an accessible but secure place away from the touch of other people, such as in a drawer.

2. Wear or hide it in a pocket or purse when you go to church, attend spiritual meetings or uplifting concerts, get together with friendly people, or visit beautiful places in nature. Doing so encodes higher vibrational levels in yourself and your totem.

3. Use the subject matter or nature of the object to enhance your self-confidence and positive thinking. For example, concentrate on the help received from your totem when you touch, see it or think of it.

4. The single most important emotional state and powerful single word to obtain personal dominion (power) is *joy*. The state of joy, bliss, samadha, in whatever language, heals body, mind and soul. If you could maintain the emotional state of joy, you would obtain everything in the world you ever wanted with little effort.

Unfortunately, human beings have memory banks of fear and primitive survival defenses that make joy almost impossible to maintain. But—whenever and however you do it—it helps cancel out the thousands of negative messages we give ourselves daily! Faith in yourself and a higher power will help you obtain inner peace.

There are no easy guidelines and clear directions for changing unconscious patterns. At times, we are at the mercy of our own weaknesses, terrors, and self-defeating behaviors. They control our behavior more than is generally admitted. Typically, our behaviors consist of ninety to ninety-five percent automatic, unconscious habits. To break undesired or ineffectual behavior, absolute determination and steady persistence are required.

When you assume responsibility for yourself and your life, you are claiming your right to have power and happiness. Thought is energy and what the mind believes changes the cellular structure of the body. Desire increases the intensity of the mind energy to actually manifest these wishes in people's lives.

## DAILY TOTEM
## POWER RITUALS

Increase positive daily habits and automatic behaviors to combat unconscious or fearful self-defeating behaviors. Double or triple your self-improvement by doing numerous faith and power totems during the day. Adopt these suggestions or create your own:

*Morning:* Stick you lucky totem or totem symbol in your pocket if you are leaving the house. If staying home, place your totem where you will notice it during the day. If you have totem jewelry, be sure to wear it (inside your clothes if you don't want it seen). Use a special scent if relevant. Carry your special book or picture with you if it is your totem.

*Daily:* Always have a representative reminder of your totem at home, in your workplace, and in your car if possible. Don't tell anyone of its meaning for you. If appropriate, place a symbol of the totem on the telephone, your billfold, bathroom mirror or some other frequently used item.

*Before Bedtime:* Sniff your selection of aromatherapy remedies or favorite scent. Sleep with a totem by your bedside or read inspirational books or articles. Note: Do not watch or read horror stories with bizarre, discouraging or brutal themes, as they will stay in your unconscious all night.

Instead go to sleep with a repetitive positive affirmation

tape you have purchased or made yourself. Avoid tapes with sub-liminal messages unless you know what you will hear. Be sure there are no negative statements because the unconscious only hears the *action* word. For example, don't tell your children, "Don't *forget* to feed the dog!" The correct suggestion is, "*Remember* to fed the dog!"

*All the Time:* Place a lucky coin, small green stone, or tiny totem in your purse or wallet to remind you of your power and prosperity.

### CLAIMING YOUR OWN POWER

Claiming your right to be happy and have dominion (power) doesn't mean you hurt or rule over other people. It means you claim your right as a spiritual person to live a fulfilled life, to experience joy, to have positive relationships and to develop your own unique talents and skills.

For those of us living in countries not at war or experiencing famine (where survival skills take precedence over personal fulfillment), one may have the luxury of working on personal evolution and self-improvement. Working on transformation and growth of the soul can be difficult and scary as change usually brings on anxiety. Giving up old habits requires immense effort.

All the herbs and medicines won't cure you if you don't want to get well or you have self-defeating behaviors and thoughts which make you sick. This is the central meaning of this chapter, which deals with the "medicine" or power base for healing. Mind and body work together.

## Power Herbs

Begin to experiment with power herbs to see if they can be useful. Begin with one or two at a time and use them long enough to determine their effects before you try another. Read the descriptions and choose one that seems to "call out" to you. Muscle-test the effectiveness of the herb if you wish. Remember, herbs are drugs if they have an effect on the body. Use them in moderation. As with all herbs and foods in general, diabetics should always check with their medical doctor before use.

## Muscle Testing

If you have a friend or health practitioner that does muscle testing (kinesiology), have him test the herb on you before using to verify its effectiveness on your body. If you don't have the herb with you, write down the name of the herb or product on a piece of paper and test with that while holding the paper in your right hand. Have a friend supply gentle energy to your left arm as it is extended parallel out from your body to the side at about shoulder height, with your elbow straight and your palm down. Let your friend gently apply pressure slightly above your left wrist to test your natural strength. Push up and down so it is obvious how much natural pressure your arm takes.

Test several herbs or products at the same time and choose at random so you won't know which is being tested. Close your eyes or fold paper over so you can't read the names. If your arm holds strong, the herb would be good for you or helpful. If your arm weakens, the herb will weaken or not be effective.

For a large person testing a small one, subtle pressure is applied as, obviously, a brawny person could force down a weaker person's arm if he wanted to induce a false negative. To test the muscle-testing process before the herb test, write "table sugar" on a piece of paper (will weaken) and a power food like "raw wheat germ" or "sardines" on another (arm will hold firm) so you can have proof that the test works.

Muscle testing can be used on any food or medicine.

## Saw Palmetto
(Serenoa serrulata)

Indigenous to southern portions of the United States, saw pal-metto is now available in health-food and grocery stores in cap-sule and leaf form. Native Americans discovered animals who ate the berries appeared healthier. Consequently Indians ate saw palmetto berries and used them to treat a variety of disorders ranging from digestive problems to mental tension.

Saw palmetto has a propensity to soothe and heal mucous membranes and may regulate and cleanse the female and male sexual organs. Herbalists recommend it for middle-aged and older men to prevent prostate problems. Some women find that it increases their breast size and may add curves. It appears to have a magical "balancing effect" on the male and female parts of the anatomy. In other words, it makes the body more attractive by adding curves to thin bodies and redistributing fat in heavier bodies.

Saw palmetto may increase sexual performance and fre-quency. The essential oil in the berries may regulate hormonal functioning or just keep sexual organs cleansed enough to keep them healthy. Since the lower part of the body is where the grounding, or foundation, of your body is located, this herb can only help your power base. Follow dosage directions on the bottle and adjust according to your own experience. Depending on your age and physical condition, results will vary.

## Licorice
(GLYCYRRHIZA GLABRA)

Licorice root, used by Native Americans to flavor teas, tobacco, and other foods, assisted in healing coughs and physical problems in general. Because it has a sweet taste, it was a favorite addition to drinks.

Today we know it contains a natural cortisone and consequently aids the body in healing in general. The cortisone in our bodies is regulated by the adrenal glands. Herbalists believe licorice helps the adrenals and the pancreas to regulate blood sugar levels and stress reactions. Americans tend to live high-stress lives and exhaust their adrenal glands prematurely. Synthetic cortisone or steroids, prized by weight lifters and other people interested in increasing their physical power and musculature, experience serious side effects with long-term use. Steroids eventually begin to have the opposite effect, tearing the body down as damage is done to tissue and membranes.

Licorice can be purchased in herbal or candy form. Don't believe licorice candy actually contains licorice unless you check the label, as ordinarily the candy is artificially flavored. Don't buy it heavily sweetened because large amounts of sugar will negate any benefits to your pancreas. Use the candy as a treat and, if in need of healing, take capsules or brew licorice leaves into a tea. No herb with natural cortisone should be taken in doses large enough to produce headaches after use.

## Wild Ram Root
(DIOSCOREA VILLOSA)

Wild yam eased colic in Indian babies and sore joints in their elders. Today we know that wild yam, especially the Mexican variety, contains natural cortisone. Like licorice, wild yam root is a natural healer and is recommended for all types of physical problems. In herbal formula remedies, it is sometimes combined with raw adrenal gland extract.

Yam root has the added advantage of being a relaxant and has antispasmodic properties which make it soothing. Like all powerful herbs, dosage should be regulated and more doesn't mean better. Unfortunately, the popularity and well-known healing properties have increased demand for this herb so it is now expensive—unless you compare it to prescription-drug costs. The suggested dosage for an average person is one or two capsules a day. For those with health problems, take twice that amount. The tincture is the easiest to take and absorb. Take one half a dropper once or twice a day.

Like all powerful herbs, it should be kept out of the reach of children.

## Hawthorn Berry
(CRATAEGNUS OXYACANTHA)

This herb is included because it nurtures a strong heart—the power center of the body. Native Americans used hawthorn berry to treat a variety of ailments, including female problems and wounds, as well as for a heart tonic. It was also eaten as a food. Today it is thought to dilate the coronary blood vessels enough to help build up the wall of the heart muscle. It also tones muscle tissue in other areas of the body and athletes include it in their vitamin regimen. The herb is readily available in health and grocery stores. Try it for emotional wounding of the heart and grieving. Use in capsule or tincture form. The regular dosage is two capsules twice a day, or one dropperful of hawthorn tincture once or twice a day.

# Ginseng
## (Panax quinquefolium)

Shaped like male genitalia, ginseng was regarded by some as an aphrodisiac and accounted for many a tale of longevity and potency. The power of this herb, if for no reason other than the positive thought energies which surrounded it over the centuries, is considerable. The Chinese called the root *Jin-chen,* which means "like a man." The American Indian name for the plant was *garantoquen,* which means "the big man"!

While ginseng never achieved the popularity with Native Americans as a wonder herb, as it had with the Chinese, both groups used the panax genre for treating similar ailments on continents thousands of miles apart. Both the Chinese and East Coast Indian tribes like the Delaware used it to treat "female" problems, to increase fertility in men, to treat sores in the mouth and throat, to help coughs and to maintain or restore good health as a general tonic. Medicine healers used it for love potions and to increase the power of other healing herbs. Because of foreign demand for the herb, Native Americans traded it with Europeans. Today, the wild herb is threatened with extinction on three continents, especially Asia; it is grown commercially, but its slow growth makes it pricey.

It is currently added to health drinks and sold in bottles resembling soda pop. It is also sold as an energizer in tablet and capsule form. Experiment and draw your own conclusions.

# 2 Sacred Herbs

Praying with the Sacred Pipe after offering it to the four directions, heaven and earth, is done by a considerable number of Lakota people. This is the common use of the Pipe not reserved to the specialist, that is, the medicine or yuwipi man. This is the way I pray with the Pipe. The Pipe is always filled with tobacco and sealed with sage. In a simple prayer the Pipe is usually not smoked. Individual Lakota pray privately in this manner out of personal devotion and on public occasions as a prayer of thanksgiving or petition.[7]

As described by the Native American Holy Woman, The White Buffalo Maiden, the pipe is a sacred symbolic representation of the Earth, a sacred entity, the mother and Grandmother. The pipe was to be used in prayer and respect for the Earth. The carving in the stone of the pipe was of the buffalo calf, a symbol for all the animals of the earth. The wooden stem represented the plants and trees.[8]

The pipe was sacred and was used unsmoked as a symbol. Tobacco and other sacred herbs were offered through the pipe as symbols of the benefits derived from spiritual helpers sustaining life and grace; it represented gratitude for help received. Promises made with the pipe represented the highest integrity and were considered binding—never to be broken.

The pipe served as a sacred tool for ritualistic offerings through the shaman's body as it represented his people. The term "pipe holder" is reserved for those individuals with the ability to have special religious powers considered honorable enough to use and smoke sacred herbal offerings.

Sacred herbs, smoked in a pipe or offered as prayer bundles, helped the medicine man to achieve an altered state of consciousness. It was a sacrament that represented honor and hopefully delivered "grace" if offered in a humble manner by a spiritual person. The holy man or woman left his or her body to perform miracles or visit distance places.

Leaving the Earth to travel to distant galaxies and spiritual planes enabled the prophet to gather information useful for survival, such as how to provide adequate food supplies and handle four-legged enemies. Medicine men and woman experienced great prophetic dreams and visions during such ceremonies, entering a dimension where physical time and space do not exist. Religious leaders around the world increasingly believe communication beyond the ordinary realms is possible. Today the American Indian Church is legally sanctioned to use peyote in their ceremonies to promote visions.

## Herbal Spirits

> If, in truth, you make good offerings of tobacco to your plants, if you give many feasts in their honor, and if you then ask your medicines to put forth their strength, and if, in addition, you talk to them like human beings, then most certainly will these plants do for you what you ask.
> —A Winnebago Indian[9]

Plants and foodstuff, considered to have spirit or soul blessed their fellow beings, the humans. The kingdom of plants vibrated and pulsated with living energy and awareness. Considered as powerful as animal and nature spirits, they were accorded respect. Humble requests and prayers given during sacred herb sacraments impressed the plant beings and assured cooperation in the future. The traditional Native American handled plants with care, cognizant of plant feelings and emotions. They believed that plant spirits reacted beneficially when pleased and refused to heal or assist when insulted.

Interestingly, the plant spirits preferred plant offerings like tobacco, lobelia, and sage over mineral or animal dedications. Tobacco, because of its preferred status by the Beings and its own powerful Plant Spirit, was held in the highest regard and status.

Great Spirit helpers attracted to sage or tobacco offerings granted requests from the shaman. Native American leaders used ritual and prayer to offer spiritual herbs before healing commenced, during ceremonies and for appreciation of help received.

Native Americans didn't distinguish between the healing characteristics or spiritual aspects of a plant because, without favor from the particular Being, the chemical properties of the herb were ineffective.

During pipe ceremonies, tobacco or sage didn't have to be smoked personally or burned for smoke. It was presented in prayer bundles, given as a healing herb, presented as a sacred gift in the form of incense, laid on altars, or buried in the ground as a gift to Mother Earth. Indians believed Plant Beings enjoyed food and other treats as well. Earlier, natives enjoying their own harvests (not government rations) routinely included the Plant Beings at their meals, always giving them their own portions.

The first step in religious ceremony was the offering of sacred plants, which displayed respect and good will toward such higher spiritual forces as Earthmother. Religions around the world offer sacred herbs in religious ceremonies. Lighting incense or candles or leaving gifts at altars in churches and cathedrals have been universal practices throughout history.

Sacred herbs also purified the shaman, the patient and the surrounding environment. In short, using the leaves of certain plants and trees occupied an important role in Indian society and still does to this day.

For modern-day Native Americans and Anglo-Americans interested in the practice of traditional Indian ritual and culture, the purchasing of tobacco or sage for offerings during ceremony is de rigueur. Included in a shaman's medicine bundle to this day, tobacco is still considered appropriate as part of your payment for traditional Native American medicine. A healer also appreciates money, meat and needed supplies. The few remaining traditional medicine men and women are not wealthy. Modern shamans will specify an amount to pay for each service.

Habitual daily tobacco smoking by Native Americans didn't occur until traditional ceremonial procedures lessened or became forbidden, or until supplies became plentiful enough for physical addictions to develop.

Daily use of tobacco violated sacred pipe rituals and displayed a lack of respect to the plant spirits who could affect the welfare of the tribe by refusing to give valuable information for survival and well-being. Shamans today believe that smoking sacred herbs daily doesn't attract Indian spirits, but rather repels valuable guidance, as the practice becomes commonplace instead of religious.

Originally, tobacco was mixed with sage, sweet grass, red willow, licorice, marjoram or other pleasant-smelling or -tasting herbs to make the smoke or calumet have a milder taste and to save tobacco supplies. Natural indigenous tobacco was strong and used sparingly. Less sacred herbs, perhaps mixed with tobacco, were smoked in corn husks, black jack leaves and later in reeds and pipes. Among these herbs were angelica, bearberry, mullein, sweet flag root, sweet grass, sumac and corn silk.

## Dreams and Visions

One day, with a crowd gathered for some occasion, Sitting Bull arose and announced that he must withdraw to give force to a vision. He walked away from the people and sang. As he sang, he saw a ball of fire approaching the village. He performed the pipe ceremony and declared that *in the smoke he saw a battle with enemy Indians in two days with many enemies killed and some Sioux as well.* Doubters, he said, should simply wait two days and see for themselves. The next morning another holy man went out and in another vision saw an enemy camp to the north. Scouts probed northward and discovered a Flathead camp in the valley of the Musselshell River.[10]

## SITTING BULL

The great Dakota chief and medicine man Sitting Bull was an unusual figure in history. He acted as tribal chief, war chief, and medicine man for his people. He displayed unusual kindness and generosity and needed no display of pomp and circumstance to set himself off as undisputed leader. And if that weren't enough, he was a prophet with unusual psychic skills. Ordinarily, three different people played these roles for the tribe, as each required great skill and specialized training.

Sitting Bull performed these roles as needed for his Teton Dakota people during the time Indian nations experienced oppression and change in all areas of their lives. His life provided many illustrations of holistic living and healing: a living legend and example of courage, mental acuity, physical and spiritual health.

Sitting Bull was famous for the visions he had awake and asleep. Before we discuss the dream that appears in all the history books, let's review one equally as accurate through the eyes of a typical young warrior.

## RUNS TOO FAST WATCHES SITTING BULL

Looking back on his most recent experience as a warrior against the Flathead, Runs Too Fast remembered he hadn't feared the encounter. He believed Sitting Bull's prophesy had given him courage, for two days before the event, the spiritual leader performed a pipe ceremony and forecast a victory.

Such was the way with Wichasha Wakan (holy men with direct access to the Great Power). What happened during raids and wars occurred according to a plan led by the Great Spirit. Death reached out when it was a warrior's time to join the other courageous braves in a beautiful hunting land of plenty. Only cowards roamed at night in anguish on a barren earth ruled by evil spirits.

Besides, Runs Too Fast had no dream of dying, and a feeling told him Sitting Bull would have known and warned him to be careful as he was still one of the youngest warriors. He remembered as a young boy that warriors who dreamed death in the next battle often dressed for the occasion and took extra care to be excessively aggressive to demonstrate bravery. Courage guaranteed they wouldn't remain on earth after death.

Visions by those with medicine only revealed what the tribe needed to know. Sometimes a powerful Wichasha Wakan like Sitting Bull received direct warning and directions about specific events to occur. Other times the visions or dreams were veiled or symbolic and one waited until it happened to know the outcome.

Runs Too Fast wanted to be like Sitting Bull more than

anything else in the world. He knew him to be a true Wichasha Wakan, a truly noble man, favored by The Great Spirit. Runs Too Fast wanted to learn the sacred ceremonies and to be a pipe carrier so he could divine information from the ancestors who lived above in the beautiful rainbow bridge in the stars.

Runs Too Fast tried not to stare at his beloved chief as it indicated rudeness, but how then could he learn to be a powerful medicine man? Several weeks later Runs Too Fast got a chance to observe his beloved idol as the holy man prepared for the biggest challenge of his life: to protect his tribe from the "White Eyes."

As Sitting Bull left the village to climb a high plateau to have his vision, Runs Too Fast noticed he carried tobacco offerings wrapped in sage tied to cherry branches. He carried his medicine bundle and appeared weary. Watching from a distance, Runs Too Fast could see Sitting Bull as a distant figure raising his arms with a decorated pipe to the four directions. Faintly he thought he heard a prayer song. Soon he could no longer see Sitting Bull but later he learned he had lain down and dreamed a vision.

Back in the village, Runs Too Fast waited patiently for his idol and tribal leader to return from his vision. There seemed to be a change in the village. During Runs Too Fast's childhood the enemy to fight were enemy Indians. Now, a new adversary approached and, true to form, Sitting Bull prophesied the identity: the long knives (white government soldiers with guns).

That night, because he counted coup, Runs Too Fast attended the important meeting of tribal elders and warriors, fascinated as Sitting Bull told of his dream.

## A True Story of Sitting Bull's Famous Dream

An insistent force drew Sitting Bull to the top of a nearby butte to commune with Wakantanka. Seated on a moss-covered rock praying and meditating, he fell asleep and dreamed.

*He saw a great dust storm propelled by high winds approaching from the east. Sailing smoothly in the opposite direction was a white cloud resembling an Indian village.... Fiercely the gale charged toward the cloud, and behind the storm Sitting Bull could see rank on rank of soldiers, their weapons and horse trimmings glinting in the sun. The tempest smashed into the cloud. Thunder pealed, lightning crackled, and great sheets of rain poured. Then the storm died out and the dust dissipated, leaving the cloud intact.*[11]

Sitting Bull predicted the village, attacked by soldiers, would survive and the Indians would win a great victory. He warned the warriors to watch for enemies approaching from the east.

Several days later Sitting Bull asked three elders to join him in a prolonged pipe ceremony. During the pipe ceremony he asked for peace among the tribes and for food, promising to sun-dance for the favor. Later, during the sun dance in which he had one hundred tiny pieces of flesh removed from his arms, he saw soldiers who had no ears standing upside down, again indicating a victory for the tribe. Sitting Bull interpreted that no ears meant the white man had no intention of honoring the treaties. Upside down meant the soldiers would all fall in defeat.[12]

Three weeks later, at the Battle of Little Bighorn, Indians killed 263 soldiers, including every one of General George Custer's soldiers. The Indians lost about three dozen braves, plus more were wounded.

# Preparing an Altar for Help

Spiritual or religious altars are frequently in the homes of success-ful people like Candace Bergen. To begin *your* communication with your higher power or, if you prefer, your higher self, prepare an altar. You will need:

1. An offering of sacred herbs, incense or oil. For Indian spirit help, include sage, tobacco, lobelia, red willow, pinon, juniper or sweet grass.
2. Your totem, or a symbol of your totem
3. A candle
4. A bird feather
5. A special rock, mineral stone or gem
6. A tiny portion of rainwater, mineral water, or holy water
7. A favorite or beloved object
8. A written prayer, request or wish.

To be in the proper state of mind you need:

1. An emotional desire to improve your life and motives (for the good of all)
2. A willingness to "Let go, let God," surrender to changes in your life, to "Go with the flow", to quit trying to swim upstream.
3. The faith and knowledge and absolute positive *state of mind* that your path will be guided and knowledge about what you're supposed to do will be given. You are here on this planet for a reason. You have a raison d'etre: reason for being.

The ingredients listed above for your altar include repre-sentations for the four directions and for the four elements: earth, air, fire and water. The impetus, or force, that will make your prayer or request work are the three necessary emotional states. The necessary mental states help propel your energy along the desired path.

Negativity from you can undo even the most powerful ritual and request. In fact, some unanswered prayers are a result of the person not being ready for it! What you believe will happen, happens, including negative outcomes. If you had a way of counting the fears and negative thoughts you give out on a daily basis (one estimate is sixty thousand a day!), you would understand the importance of always having faith in your dreams. Our primitive brain stem reacts only to preserve the status quo of primordial memory traces which are no longer appropriate for contemporary man.

To prepare your altar, place it in as private a place as possible. Leave it out or put it in a container that can be brought out easily. Use it daily, preferably morning and night. Native Americans and Eastern holy men often face their altars to the east because this is the direction from which the morning sun rises and begins each new day. Timing your prayers is important, too. The new and full moons are seen as powerful times to start a new project (new moon) and to bring into fruition an old one (full moon).

Repeat out loud your request or prayer. Remember to add the words "For the good of all" after your request so you do not inadvertently attempt to manipulate another human being. Even when doing a healing for another, it is best to obtain the person's consent first or, if impossible, ask that the healing be done only if it is "right for them at this time."

Sage, tobacco, or herbs such as sweet grass need not be lit to be an offering but then another pleasant smell—a scented candle or oil—is needed. Burning tiny pinches of sage or small white sage smudging sticks are nice indoors.

For your home altar use prepared incense sticks or cones. Pinon cones are a wonderful aromatic treat and attract Native

American guides. Experiment until you find your favorite. Sandalwood is favored by angels and all spirit helpers.

Candles should be lit just before you use them and blown out as soon as you are through. Candles attract guides from the unseen world that surrounds us and are recognized by religions around the world for this purpose. Select from white, purple, indigo, blue, gold, or yellow candles. You need only one. Let your instinct or "knowing" select the candle color you use.

If you are requesting a healing for yourself or another, use or include an orange or green candle. Red ones shouldn't be used unless you are in a depression that is not caused by a physical illness. For relationship or family problems use as many as needed to represent each person.

Small candles cost more and don't last long, but offer more color variety. Large candles in heavy glass bought at the grocery or religious store are the safest and least expensive. When home, keep a candle burning to remind you of your increased faith and strength and to attract angel helpers. Place your car keys by the candle so you will remember to blow it out when you leave. Do not place candles near blowing paper or curtains or where pets or small children can get at them!

Your altar may be covered with a special cloth before laying your implements on it, or it may be covered after each use, as you desire.

*Wake-up Call*: At your altar every morning, recite your desired wish, prayer, or positive affirmation.

*Before Bedtime*: Repeat your need for help or healing or positive power statement right before bedtime. If you have time, light your candle or use incense in the morning and night.

# How to Have a Vision

One of the seemingly magical gifts a medicine man or woman demonstrated was predicting the future. This is a gift now available to many people.

Your "sixth sense" or unconscious knows exactly what will happen in a certain situation if you allow that message to come through. However, magical gifts of prophecy disappear or come back to harm you (what goes around comes around) if used in a manipulative or selfish way. For this reason, only people desiring or having done personal growth work are handed this gift.

At first, the ability to divine is treacherous at best because people tend to see and hear what satisfies their wishes. If you get messages or see visions that are too good to be true, they probably are.

Experimenting with trying to improve your clairvoyant skills is a fascinating hobby that can do nothing but improve your life even when you are wrong. Errors point out where you went wrong and what interfered with the correct perception. "Knowing" what will happen doesn't prevent the occurrence if it is a karmic lesson, but you will be better prepared to handle the event. The "gift of sight" is only given to those who will not use the information for self-promotion. Information from a channel for a spiritual voice will not give you material that would change your soul's journey.

Nonethical or uninformed psychics can give you incorrect data that is destructive to your welfare. Even the best psychics, when they are "on," are only accurate eighty-five to ninety percent of the time. Receiving money, doing too many readings, and knowing the client personally are all dangers to an accurate reading because the psychic is personally involved with and wanting to please the client. Think about how much you want your own heartfelt desires!!!

With these warnings in mind, now let's work on becoming a

visionary. Be sure to light a sacred herb or incense before you begin. Aromas trigger unconscious memories and feelings in the brain which help bring needed material to the surface. If desired, drink some herbal tea made from the "nerve herbs" listed in chapter four. Use tea bags or tincture or take capsules of the nervine with a warm drink.

1.  Sit down alone in a quiet place with *no direct question or request on your mind*. Ask only for guidance from a higher power or your higher self. Have a pencil and a piece of paper with you.

2.  Do whatever it takes to blank out your mind as much as possible, knowing thoughts will come in and out of consciousness.

3.  Sitting quietly by yourself whether taking a bath, smoking a pipe, listening to "white noise" such as a fan, petting your dog, or just resting in the woods or on your own porch are examples of activities which allow the left brain or logical mind-set to temporarily slow down. The right-brain begins to intuit and naturally create. Put all active problem-solving thinking as far away as possible. If you have trouble clearing your mind, meditate, take a bath or lie down, playing soothing music before beginning.

4.  Now, while watching your fishing line, sitting by a tree, or feeling the top of your dog's head, try to have a "no-brainer" as you do your relaxed activities. Later, when you find yourself thinking, write down the thought. Repeat the clearing of your mind and then writing down what you find yourself thinking next.

    Now you have your WHAT, a topic in which you are currently in need of help. It doesn't matter if it seems unimportant or is nonsensical; it may be a symbol of an important issue.

5. Now, regardless of where you are or what you are doing, look around again, totally uninterested in the result. What do you see around you? Look to the clouds and see if you see a picture in them. If you are around water, watch for pictures in the waves or in the sand. If you are around birds, notice what kind you see and what they are doing with each other.[13] If you are sitting on your deck, look for emblems or pictures in the wood. If you are inside your home, glance at familiar paintings, statues or figurines to see if you see something in them you hadn't noticed before. If your eyes are closed, be aware of any thoughts or events that pop into your mind. *Your unconscious, or sixth sense, will present you with information* much like a Rorschach blot on a personality test. You will see something new, have a thought, or "know" or feel an emotion. This is HOW this situation will turn out.

6. Be aware that each person has his or her personal "open window" or means for using psychic abilities. With practice, some people can shut their eyes and see pictures, while others feel or sense information. People with psychic talent often prefer to use playing or tarot cards, read palms, or gaze into an object like a crystal. The unconscious sees in these objects something of importance. Experiment with your psychic talent because it may be entirely different in method from others.

7. After your experience, write your results in a notebook. What was the problem and what was the single most important thought or discovery you were given to solve the problem?

8. Dreaming will often answer a question or tell you of an approaching problem. Start a dream notebook in which you record yours. Dreaming of events is often prophetic of events which will occur in the next several days to usually

no more than six weeks. A life-changing event may be fore-cast six months ahead. For dreaming solutions to a problem, ask yourself before you go to sleep to dream the answer to a problem.

When discovering information, if you find fears and or tears arise, stay with the feelings and let them surface. Concentrate on expressing them: don't try to cover up or suppress your emotions. This will be the most important step in working out your solutions. Before new and better experiences in your life emerge, it is necessary and often painful to clear away the feeling blocking your progress. Remember, energy can't be destroyed, it only changes form. Repressing or suppressing anger, fear, guilt, or grief doesn't get rid of these feelings; they only seek expression in more unconscious and destructive ways.

After allowing these emotions to surface, you can work through them and then continue progressing in your life toward bigger and better things. Often, in order to make opportunities in life or alter negative behavior patterns, a drastic change is needed in yourself. Don't think changing someone else is going to do it for you. It won't. If a pattern in your life is destructive, you are the common denominator. If you keep doing what you have always done, you are going to get what you've always gotten. Ask for guidance and you will get it.

## Tobacco

Tobacco, indigenous to the "new world," was eventually culti-vated by Indians. Their cultivation patterns, uncovered by archaeologists excavating ancient Indian sites, help determine early Indian migration and trade routes. Columbus eagerly brought tobacco back to Spain as one of his discoveries and, within a hundred years, its use had spread to all of Europe.[14]

This is perhaps a retribution for the firewater addiction

they brought to the Americas, which has ruined more lives than could ever be estimated. Native Americans, probably because of their spiritual interest in altered states and a unique chemical reaction, have had an enormous battle with alcohol addiction.

Tobacco originated with the Native Americans as an herb used for healing and sacraments. Today, because of widespread addiction and consequent health problems, the consensus is that tobacco is not suitable for daily inhaling. It shouldn't be inhaled or chewed. Unless you are a medicine healer or a pipe carrier, it is best used as a spiritual offering or wrapped in cloth for tiny prayer bundles.

Tobacco is still commonly used by Native American shamans, whose opinions on its use vary. Some are addicted, yet it doesn't diminish their power. In my experience, modern medicine people use tobacco sparingly or only ceremonially, believing constant use does not attract spirit helpers as it becomes commonplace. Old timers do their work as they were taught and accomplish healing whether they smoke or not. Shamans who aren't addicted use tobacco for pipe ceremonies, to clear their own aura, or to achieve an altered state of consciousness so they can prophesy.

In the pipe ceremony, tobacco may be replaced by or cut with sage, sweet grass, licorice or any of the herbs mentioned previously. When mixed with other herbs, the pipe contents were called *kinnikinnik*, an Algonquian word meaning that which is mixed. Rituals often took place at special times of the month or at a seasonal solstice or equinox. Sage is the favored supplement or replacement for tobacco.

Why do people smoke? There are validated studies showing that smoking improves concentration and memory, even among smokers.[15] One would guess it would have more punch for nonsmokers who use it for increased awareness. Unfortunately, it also pollutes from within and is a major cause of disease.

Nicotine, like caffeine, is one of the most addictive substances known to man. It affects brain-wave function, alters mood, and serves as a biological reward (physically and mentally rewarding) for humans and laboratory animals.

People with addictions to these substances have to increase the dosages to get the same effect and suffer withdrawal if they don't continue use. Too much caffeine brings on anxiety and eventually cancels out increased clarity. Try skipping your morning coffee and you get a headache or diminished mental acuity. Add an extra cup when needed (not daily) and receive extra thinking power (provided you aren't drinking too much to begin with).

Tobacco achieved success as a healing aid because it was used only when needed. Remember, there were no pain killers and synthetic morphine, and no pharmacies, in early America. Original tobacco was strong, and Native Americans used it to discharge mucous and dilate congested lungs, bronchial tubes, and ear canals. Nicotine contains norepinephrine, which dilates mucous membranes, speeds heart rate and stimulates the adrenal gland. In a severely ill patient, without modern antibiotics, the tobacco might prevent congestive heart failure for patients with fluid in the lungs.

Morphine, quinine, codeine, nicotine, caffeine, mescaline, and lobaline are all part of a diverse nitrogen-containing substance family produced by plants known as alkaloids. Today these drugs are used in medical situations in standard contemporary practice, as well as by shamans.

Childhood addiction to caffeine is epidemic and an unrecognized national problem!

Because tobacco has concentrated alkaloids, Native Americans used it as a disinfectant to treat wounds. It was also used to relieve pain. In early medicine, datura (*Datura stramonium* or "jimson weed") and sage (and/or tobacco) were used as a smoking mixture for asthma and tuberculosis, and no doubt provided some type of relief.

For religious use tobacco was ingested or drunk with datura (to induce vomiting for purifying before a ceremony). Tobacco and datura are poisonous when ingested.

Jimson weed is called "locoweed" by farmers—familiar with the effects on their cattle after eating it. Overdoses from datura ingestion in people trying to have hallucinations have resulted in deaths and account for increased admittals of teenagers in emergency rooms. Chemical companies today use condensed ingredients from nicotine to make a powerful insecticide, but nicotine is also added to pharmaceutical drugs to increase their effect.

Children shouldn't be around tobacco smoke due to the secondhand smoke effects. The habitual breathing of tobacco smoke creates toxic levels of nicotine and tar (creosote) in the lungs. If that isn't enough, contemporary cigarettes also contain saltpeter, formaldehyde and other chemicals that cause disease and impotence.

For shamans and smokers, The Santa Fe Natural Tobacco Co. in Santa Fe, New Mexico, has a variety of natural and organic tobaccos as well as sage sticks and herbal blends. Regular tobacco companies are beginning to offer their version of "pure tobacco." Pregnant women shouldn't smoke tobacco or use herbs unless its use is prescribed by their medical doctors or certified natural health practitioners.

Gentian, myrtle, magnolia, slippery elms and the nervines are reported to help those trying to break the nicotine habit. These herbs can be taken in capsules or drunk as a tea. Gentian root is chewed at intervals as needed.

# Sage

While sage is second to tobacco as *the* prized sacred offering, it is *first* for versatility and health benefits. Different uses are:

1. Seasonings for foods
2. Herbal healing plants for assorted physical problems
3. Smoked, burned for smudging and used in Indian ceremonies.

It was and still is prized by Native Americans for its aromatic and sacred qualities and is easily available. Today it is widely used by shamans. As with juniper, sage is a versatile and valuable ceremonial herb. So far, neither is an endangered species. Sage is discussed in chapter three as it ranks first today as a clearing herb for smudging.

# Lobelia

(LOBELIA INFLATA)

Lobelia was called Indian Tobacco by early settlers who observed its use by Native Americans. Seminole and Creek tribes of Oklahoma (after translocation) called it Little Tobacco, or Old Man's Tobacco. Indians believed it had spiritual and magical qualities and used it ceremonially. Today naturopathic healers call it the "herb with a brain" for its quality of enhancing the effectiveness of other herbs when used in combination with them.

Chemically, lobelia resembles tobacco in that both contain alkaloids (lobaline in lobelia, nicotine in tobacco) and are strong taken in quantity (a little goes a long way). Both herbs stimulate in small doses and act as relaxants in large doses. If you take too much, both are emetics (cause vomiting). In appearance, the lobelia plant resembles tobacco, but is only about ten inches high.

It was probably called the "Old Man's Tobacco" because it was rare, sacred and used in ceremonies by tribal male elders.

Howard found in his research that, according to legend, Creeks found their first lobelia growing on the grave of an *Ispokogi*, a spirit from the Source of Life itself. The following describes a religious ritual performed by Oklahoma Native Americans offering lobelia to the river.

> They all put a grain of the old man's tobacco on their heads and in each ear. Then, at a signal given, four different times, they throw some into the river, and every man at a like signal plunges into the river and picks up four stones from the bottom....[16]

Lobelia is a highly effective and versatile herb and has been used for internal and external healing for varied health problems. In previous centuries it was used to treat serious diseases and its scientific name, "siphilitica," denotes the disease.

According to the literature of the time, Native Americans used lobelia to cure syphilis and gonorrhea brought over by the Europeans. It is considered to be a powerful herb with strong narcotic properties. Michael Weiner, in his book *Earth Medicine Earth Food*, notes that European physicians did not obtain the cure for the venereal disease, as had been rumored by Native American healers. Listed as possible reasons for the success of Indians were the facts that they used the herb fresh as opposed to dried and administered it in combination with other herbs such as the bark of the wild cherry tree. Physicians didn't consider better health practices and spiritual application as variables.

Eaten fresh in large quantities it is poisonous to livestock, and large doses might render a person immobile or unconscious. Theoretically, people wouldn't eat the plant raw and, if they did, would vomit before they reached lethal doses. Lobelia may be the drug used by Voodoo doctors to render cursed people into a zombie state. Needless to say, if the herb doesn't kill them, the shock of their condition might.

Lobelia is best and most safely taken in small quantities to increase the effectiveness of another herb. Unfortunately, the FDA declared it illegal to sell lobelia in combination with another herb, but you can still buy it alone and combine it with other herbs for remedies.

Today lobelia is expensive, but a little goes a long way. It is used currently for lung problems like asthma and in combination with other herbs for respiratory ailments like mullein. It works with nervines like valerian or skullcap for anxiety, and in fact appears to enhance the efficiency of other herbal remedies if added in small doses. Use one capsule or one-half dropper (about ten drops) of lobelia tincture with another herbal mixture if applicable.

# 3 Clearing Herbs

At the new moon there is a general meeting of the medicine men called by those who...collect for a feast on this occasion. As soon as they come together they commence singing. They make a bed of coals, and then burn pine leaves, or any herb which they may have or sweet grass and thus raise a species of incense. They hold each of them their medicine bag in the smoke.[17]

Native Americans used smudging herbs to remove bad energy fields around people. Clearing herbs, offered to plant spirits, possessed special powers in getting rid of unseen, troublesome entities like ghosts or displeased beings. Smudging herbs cleansed the doctor and patient and attracted spirit helpers. This ancient ritual is still practiced today by traditional Native Americans and by anyone else who wants to purify himself or his surroundings of supernatural or malefic influences.

Smudging or clearing herbs are used to clear undesirable vibrations out of homes and off people, and to promote health.

People and places have a certain feeling or energy. People leave traces of their personalities in their homes. Entering someone's home may make you feel uplifted and vibrant. A home or property might cause an uncomfortable feeling or have a musty odor or cold spot. Real-estate agents comment on the vibrations of a house as due to the energies of previous occupants.

The uncomfortable feeling you can get when entering certain houses need not be caused by a ghost although "sensitives" believe that ghosts do leave a certain presence in a home. Because children and animals have not developed "rational thinking," they sense these vibrations more easily than adults .

It is well-known that the moods of someone with whom you are living affect your behavior and emotional state. Everyone has been around a *drainer*, or person who saps your energy. Susceptible people, usually loved ones, end up exhausted. Native Americans, especially the healers, used burning herbs and woods to help remove unwanted energies and restore strength and power.

Instructions for using cleaning and smudging herbs are given in this chapter. The average person wanting to improve his life will experiment and draw his own conclusions. But before discussing specific methods, it is useful to look at the Indians' awareness of unseen energy fields. Anthropological psychologists think that belief in the prominence of destructive forces in the Native American environment increased greatly after their way of living was interrupted by white Europeans.

Indigenous peoples believed illness, even accidents, resulted primarily from unseen forces. Negative energies in a person or his environment wreaked havoc and destruction and required dream analysis or family therapy. Shamans could solve individual and clan problems, but the dreaded illnesses resulting from spells or curses from invisible beings like ghosts or angry spirit entities terrified even the bravest and strongest warrior.

Thus, ceremonial customs accompanying herb use played a large role in contacting and attracting beneficial plant spirits or powerful beings to help eliminate undesirable energy forces.

Smoking or smudging herbs and plants purified the air and removed physical problems and malignant energies.

Three types of malefic influences were soul disorders, physical diseases, and undesirable energy forces from ghosts or evil spells. Soul disorder, defined by the Great Basin tribes Paiute and Papago as *staying sickness*,[18] came on through personal transgressions toward others or sacrilege. Transgressions toward powerful spirits resulted in serious repercussions. This type of illness differed from physical illnesses caused by injuries or accidents and from white man's diseases such as measles. Physical problems known as *wandering sickness* came and left if healed. Herbs and physical remedies, combined with the healing power of the medicine man, cured these sicknesses.

*Staying sickness* was eternal and condemned the offender to the fate sentenced him by angry spirit beings who punished. Only the strongest medicine invoked from powerful spirit beings healed anyone afflicted. Rituals and prayers prevailed. Soul sickness invaded the body and mind like an invisible cancer.

Common types of illnesses resulting from animal spirit transgressions were coyote sickness and rabbit sickness. For example, in some Great Basin tribes, pregnant women who dared to view a rabbit while pregnant suffered serious consequences during pregnancy or labor, such as miscarriage and still birth, called "rabbit sickness."

One universal method for removing unwanted energies or curses was the sucking cure. The medicine healer sucked the undesirable spirit from the body, usually using a thin tube, often a small hollow bone or animal horn. A strange object, looking like bodily tissue, spit out of the shaman's mouth confirmed the success of the surgery. The shaman chewed the appropriate herb or sage to help capture the curse, and then spit out the wad to get rid of it and convince the patient that the damage was removed. Magical medicine men spat out tissue they didn't put in their mouths!

The term *wandering sickness* was reserved for physical diseases like typhoid or cholera, brought by Europeans, that appeared suddenly and eventually left or resulted in death. Direct application of herbs treated or relieved physical symptoms of these terrible disorders against which the Native Americans had no natural immunities. It is due to their good health-habits and consequent strong constitution that there was a single Indian left after the epidemics. Tuberculosis, or indications of previous exposure, is still common today on reservations.

## Ghosts

Ghosts so frightened Indians that a deceased person's possessions were discarded and his name remained unspoken. Traditionally, a period of wailing and mourning for the person followed death and the Indians burned or gave away the deceased person's possessions. Burning possessions of the ill or deceased kept disease germs (unknown until the last century) from spreading.

The red man believed that even a wonderful person in life becomes undesirable after death. To speak the dead person's name kept the deceased from going on to the afterworld. Those whose ghostly spirit remained assured trouble and bad luck for those he knew in life

Ghosts presented problems to tribal members because they thought deceased people hung around loved ones. Survivors could grieve their loss but if they didn't let go they brought trouble to themselves and the tribe. The dead who had failed to earn a life among the ancestors in the stars were earthbound and created mischief and doom. The medicine leader was called upon to help remove ghost energies. At the same time, mourning was encouraged to help the survivors grieve and let go. Lengthy funeral ceremonies allowed survivors to express emotional pain from their losses, a healthier process than modern funerals. The author has attended funerals so formal no one cried!

## Witches

Witches terrified tribal members because they were fellow clansmen with special powers. Astonishingly, tribesmen often suspected their own shamans, in the same way religious leaders in Europe burned suspected heretic clergy at the stake. Usually, suspected witches were men, since most medicine leaders were male. Women with medicine-woman status, although less likely to occupy important ceremonial roles, also drew suspicion when tribal problems arose. Native Americans believed witches shapeshifted into animals. Unethical medicine leaders, thought to have the ability to send empowered arrows through the air, brought disease to their enemies.

Men became invisible to seduce women. Male or female witches could turn into owls, wolves, bears or other animals or birds to disguise themselves while carrying out their evil deeds. Medicine leaders were suspected because they were the only people capable of supernatural feats. Personal enemies were sometimes accused of causing chaos or bad luck, but were rarely viewed by clansmen as powerful enough to bring ruin to the tribe.

Like the early Christian and Hebrew prophets, healers who failed to stem plagues or droughts, or who made inaccurate predictions, sometimes died at the hands of their disgruntled followers. Unfortunately, Native American medicine healers experienced failures in attempts to heal European diseases for which they had no immunities. Their inability to cure shamed the

Indian healers and brought suspicion of foul play or witchcraft. Clan members believed that the doctors didn't use their powers or that they practiced black magic to bring on failure and ruin.

Even the sophisticated Cherokee found it hard to give up old beliefs. At some time during the 1800s they made it unlawful to kill a witch in animal form but not in human! Fault-finding likely resulted from projected blame for personal and tribal problems exacerbated by the devastation of their culture. Similarly, European religious zealots burned over a million witches at the stake (usually women, their children and animals).

## Native American Clearing Herbs

Native Americans, living in the open, didn't have to worry about not getting enough fresh air or breathing too much smoke. Their active lives centered around working and living in the out-of-doors. They weren't polluted from chemicals and city-living smoke and fumes. Clearing herbs, like all burning substances, should be used for specific reasons and in moderation.

Among the most popular purifying herbs and plants were cedar, juniper, sage, sweet grass, pinon, red willow and mesquite: aromatic scents which pleased the senses and the spirits. Especially appealing to nature beings were herbs prized for their aroma and smoke which ballooned into giant puffs enveloping large areas when burned. Billowing smoke from these plants rose to greet the spirit messengers.

Herbs used for inhaling or burning smoke for pleasure, ceremony or respiratory illnesses were angelica, bearberry, coltsfoot, deer's tongue, mullein, yerba santa, sumac leaves, dogwood, corn silk and valerian,[19] as well as tree barks such as laurel, squaw bush, maple bush, cherry, poplar, birch, wood betony, rose and arrowwood.

# Smudging Today

Today's contemporary shaman may use Eastern Indian incense like sandalwood, myrrh, or frankincense. Incense can be purchased in myriad scents. To assure a quality product, try to identify companies located in the region where the natural plant is grown. For example, purchase pinon processed in New Mexico or other southwestern states. Eastern incense, such as myrrh, is best obtained from companies located in India or Far Eastern countries and is readily available in America.

Aromatic herbs and plants can be purchased loose or pressed. After drying, the herbs or barks are sold loose, powdered or bundled (to make a smudge stick). Smudging plants or substances from them can be compressed to form smudging bundles, incense sticks or small cones.

Pressed cones of pinon and mesquite contain delightful aromas. To light these, hold the larger bottom of the cone with one hand while you light the pointed end of the cone with the other. After it begins to flame brightly, blow out the fire, but continue to blow on the cone to keep it smoldering. Then set the cone in a fireproof container so the sides are not touching anything which would stop the burning process.

For loose or powdered herbs, charcoal is frequently used to facilitate smoldering. Continue to baste the charcoal from time to time with herbs or their powder or oil. Flat charcoal cakes, available in religious and metaphysical stores, light easily so herbs can be placed on top. Plants and incense samples can be tested for personal preferences and comfort as well as effectiveness of results.

Large brush-sage smudging bundles should never be burned in the house around carpet or flammable objects, as sparks create a fire hazard. Even when you think you're being careful, invariably you end up with holes in the carpet. When using smudging herbs indoors, keep them in a large fireproof container and do not leave any smoldering herbs unattended.

For effectiveness, safety, aroma, ease, length of burning time and availability, it is difficult to surpass incense sticks burned in an incense holder. Indoors these are wonderful for meditation and ceremonies, especially when you do not want to stop to replenish supplies.

Using herbs outside is a different story. Use your campfire or ceremonial fire to burn woods such as pinon, mesquite, cedar or brush sage. Never cut down healthy trees: look for damaged shrubs, sticks or dead wood. Green wood doesn't burn and you contribute to the preservation of greenery on our planet when you respect trees.

There is no substitute for participating in a spiritual adventure in the wild. Today, supervised sweat lodges, rope courses, nature hikes, or camping enrich peoples' lives. Observing nature together or by yourself on a vision quest[20] can be a spiritually rejuvenating experience. Do you remember your first experience outside around a fire?

## CLEARING
## YOUR HOUSE

It is a good idea to occasionally clear your house. This is especially important after a large gathering, a party, a death in the family, a visit from an unwanted guest, a quarrel, or once-a-year during spring housecleaning.

Even a party—especially with drinking or loud talking—overstimulates because it leaves a variety of conflicting energies and thought-forms in a room when it is over. People with sensitive nervous systems or clairvoyant abilities often find they have trouble sleeping or being at peace after a fun party or a night of talking and mixing with different people. If your meeting was a religious or spiritual gathering that left your home with an uplifting or good energy you don't need to clear it.

Motel or hotel rooms often keep people awake for reasons other than dripping faucets. Think of the hundreds or thousands of people who slept in the same room! Sensitive people travel with incense and holy water to minimize these influences.

To clear a motel room, light a smudging herb, incense stick or, in an emergency, a cigar, and place it in a glass or metal container. Leave it to smoke while you open a window or door (this is important). If there is more than one room, you must open a window in every room. Incense sticks work nicely. If you travel frequently, take a spray bottle of holy water in your car and carry a sage stick and fireproof container for it. Use them each time you occupy a new room.

If a room is stale with cigarette smoke, then your use of tobacco won't clear the room and unfortunately may be a negative sign of former occupants which you probably won't clear with anything. Ask for another room.

This points out the paradox of tobacco. A little, like all powerful substances, goes a long way. Overused, it ruins or pollutes and may be a sign the room has a "history." Cigarette abuse and overuse has damaged property and people and ruined the image of tobacco in today's society.

To clear your entire home, smudge each room with sage smudging sticks or smolder incense in each room with a window open. The bad energy will go outside, where it dissipates. To clear a haunted, very old, or large house, smudging with sulfuric powder may be needed. Open all the windows and doors and vacate the premises to avoid breathing the smoke. Wear protective goggles and a painters' mask or handkerchief over your nose and mouth.

Another method of clearing a house is to use a large iron skillet in which you scorch or burn salt and then walk around the house smoking every room. This method requires enough physical strength to hold the iron skillet aloft for a while using pads to protect your hands. Outside, pouring salt around the house's foundation is a Celtic method for keeping bad energy out, as is their method of putting a mirror in a window in every room with the mirror side facing outside. If a ghost or bad energy persists ask a medium, priest, or clearing expert to help you out.

Other clearing helpers include lighting white or purple candles and using scented oils or incense like frankincense and myrrh, playing chants or Christmas music through the house while clearing and requesting, through prayer, the removal of the undesirable energy.

Rooms change vibrations with the thoughts and actions of the occupants. Landlords need to smudge their rental property after the departure of a tenant, especially an undesirable one that had to be evicted!

## Clearing Yourself
## Or Another

Clearing a person only lasts for a limited period of time. It does not guarantee the long-term success that you may have when a ghost is banished from a house (although unsavory occupants can often attract the ghost back). Therefore, the following suggestions are recommended for use when appropriate and will vary somewhat with each person. Clearing a person is an ongoing process but can prove itself invaluable.

1. Standing in the smoke of an outside fire is the quickest method to clear yourself. Now you know why it feels so good to stand by a fire. Increase power by burning pruned rose bush sticks, gathered dry or dead pinon wood, fallen willow sticks or brush sage.

2. If you are indoors, put incense or a burning herb on the floor and stand over it, fanning yourself with a fan or feather fan to make sure the smoke totally surrounds you. Use the fan to sweep your energy field or help another. To clear yourself with force: wear your totem, recite spiritual scriptures, be forceful in your desire to remove the unwanted energy. State out loud, "I am a sacred child of God," and picture yourself surrounded by golden energy.

## Need for Protection Rituals Today

The true medicine healers and today's gifted men and women can see into the fourth dimension, a plane where the unseen energies—thought forms, earthbound beings and angelic helpers—reside. Viewing the invisible world, it is easy to recognize a need for helping people protect themselves. Those who know recognize three main forces or entities against which we all need protection. The first is "leftover" vibrations still hanging around due to undesirable people, activities, or unfriendly ghosts. The clearing rituals described above eliminate this type until something negative brings it back.

The second type is "ongoing" energy vampires—usually needy family members or friends who are totally unaware of their "talent" for draining the life energy from other people. After you have been in contact with them, they feel better, you feel worse! Spouses, teen-agers, needy friends and sickly relatives are usually the innocent culprits as they have no awareness of ill intent or knowledge of the process.

The phenomenon of *drainers* is a totally foreign concept with modern people who think it only superstition. But the "rational thinking" in our culture doesn't make the phenomenon go away. Like electricity running through your TV, draining energy can run through your body even though you don't see it. One day this phenomenon will be proven by scientific experiments based on quantum physics.

*Drainers* are only able to draw your energy because you feel a need to take care of them either through guilt, need for self-punishment, or your desire to have the person around you. Being in love is one of the most powerful senders of energy from one person to another. Having sex with a person greatly increases each one's ability to connect with the other through space. You don't even have to be together to drain the other's energy!

In some cases, it is necessary to assume responsibility for a person, as a parent for his children. Small children need complete care for a long time but cannot draw energy unless the parent continually elicits it through a wish to be needed.

People sapped of their strength need to make appropriate decisions about whom and what they are responsible for and act accordingly. Because we want to be able to give and to support particular people, we need to learn to protect ourselves from losing vital strength. This self-protection has no effect on being able to love and take care of these people: in fact it improves your ability to be nurturing because you are not unduly tired and over-extended. Interestingly, people who lack nurturing skills or have the ability to detach themselves, appropriately or not, seldom have this problem. Some of the worst cases of draining affect highly spiritual people who have not learned to protect themselves from the plethora of needs of the world and average people who are vulnerable to a devastating loss or injury.

Couples, especially those in karmic relationships (known today as codependent), are especially adept at drawing energy from each other. Sleeping together is one of the best times for astral traveling and the physical proximity makes the draining process easier. Remember, most people have no idea this phenomenon is happening. Reaching out to another with an invisible cord can also occur between people who have never had sex or slept together if one or both parties desire the other with intensity. Be careful what you wish for—you might get it. Elizabeth Barrett Browning said, "God often answers our prayers, a gift with a gauntlet in it."

Naturally your susceptibility to draining increases in time of crisis, usually with one partner doing the best job of collecting energy. Usually drainers end up married or living with martyr-type personalities. Your partner cannot drain your energy unless you need the other person as badly as he or she needs you.

Alcoholics or people with addictions are especially attractive to entities. Earthbounds (ghosts) and bad thought-forms can latch on to them and drain their energy. Since the spirits aren't alive and want to experience their former habits, they try to get a person to carry out their fantasies, such as drinking, encouraging sexual encounters or taking drugs. While greatly overdone by Hollywood (being taken over by evil spirit entities that make you do things you don't want to do), it does happen with people in intoxicated or drug states because they aren't "all there." Their etheric bodies, which surround the physical, are full of holes and easily penetrated.

The Native Americans were right about the existence of undesirable energy fields such as those that might be felt in an ancient dungeon where terrible acts occurred. Some ghosts are friendly and waiting on earth for their loved ones to join them, or are confused into thinking they are still alive. The dangerous ones were murderers or those whose earthly behavior resulted in such a low vibrational state they couldn't ascend to a higher level.

Occasionally a spirit may just like it here. One famous drug-addicted singer who is frequently sighted alive may be roaming around with a spirit body dense enough to be seen by people with "the sight."

*Sensitives* can see thought-form energies like an bright aura or negative ones, which are dark and jagged. Mediums can sometimes see images of people who have just left the room.

The most important protection and clearing ritual you can do for yourself is to let go of your own addictions, habits and dependencies. Next, rid yourself of negative people, places, and things. *The worst enemy or negativity around us is the third form: our own thought forms.* They have occurred so often in our minds that the energy occupies a dense space (think of it as a dark cloud) that hangs around our head and body all the time! These thoughts, of course, are the hardest to get rid of because we tend to rerun old mental tapes over and over in our heads. Clairvoyants see these energies around our head like Medusa, with the snakes coming out of her head!

You can smoke a room from the inside, give away clothes, jewelry and furniture to get rid of vibrations, avoid bad energy scenes like seedy or low-life locations, or choose to try another spouse, but you are still stuck with your own imagination and mind.

Ninety percent of imagined enemies, ghosts, persecution complexes and paranoid states are created in our own minds, and people with these serious problems may suffer their whole lifetimes with these afflictions. The rest of us go in and out of this state as natural changes and life's problems test us over and over again. Although not recognized in our society, the lunar and astrological rotation of planets exacerbates these fears.

## Smudging Herbs

### Sage

Sage grows wild all over the United States in species ranging from large, rangy, twiggy bushes with tough leaves to small single-stemmed plants with delicate silver velvetlike leaves.

Unfortunately for lay people, even herbalists fail to distinguish between the two main unrelated varieties of herbs called sage.

First, there is the sage species (*Artemisia*), commonly known as wormwood, which includes "sage brush" and related species like *Artemisia vulgaris*, known as mugwort. The *Artemisia* varieties used by Native Americans for centuries are indigenous to America. Included in this family is the silver sage prized by Indians and often called sacred sage. This is a single stemmed plant, about nine inches tall, which grows wild in the desert as well as in temperate climates and at all altitudes. This herb grows prolifically even in poor soil. Healers recognize the male plant as different from the female plant and use each accordingly when treating the different sexes.

Second, there is the sage which is related to the mint family (*Salvia officinalis*) and is commercially cultivated and sold in grocery stores for flavoring foods like turkey dressing. It has been used by Native Americans for several centuries and grows wild throughout the United States. It, too, has variations within the species and close chemical relatives in other plant groups.

The mint variety is indigenous to Europe but has been in America for several hundred years, perhaps brought by the Spaniards. Sage occupies an important role in European and mid-Eastern herbal history. Today, both species are termed "sage" colloquially because of similar odor and characteristics. To distinguish between the two species, not to mention the varieties within the species, requires an herbologist.

Further complicating identification are the dozens of labels given by local people to the same variety of sage. For example, varieties have been called black sage, purple sage, Texas sage, little sage, women's herb, little herb, lad's love, garden sage, wild sage, blue sage, silver sage, sacred sage, chia sage, squaw-root, absinthe, lyre-leafed sage, scarlet sage, thistle sage, crimson sage, Hummingbird sage, white sage, mugwort, and sage brush.

Reference books containing Indian names for plants are usually guesswork as to which herb it is. Sage is mentioned frequently, but it is sometimes impossible to identify specific varieties. Other species unrelated to those frequently called sage were also used to treat similar disorders.

The *Artemisia frigida* variety, known as little silver sage or—by this writer—sacred sage, is often called little wild sage. Sioux call it women's medicine, *Wia-ta-pezhe*, Omaha-Ponca tribes called it little gray herb, *Pezhe-hota zhinga*, and *Kiwokki* was the term used by Pawnee.[21]

Grocery-store sage won't impress you with its aroma compared to its worthy addition to turkey. Conversely, silver sage is too pungent for dressing but adds a sacred, aromatic touch to your prayers.

Shamans, of course, always prefer natural or wild varieties for spiritual reasons and for their effectiveness outdoors. The stronger the odor, the better the herb for smudging, thus favoring the noncultivated, wild varieties. The odor comes from the presence of essential oil in the herb, the main reason for its prized medicinal qualities.

Sage, brewed for tea, should be confined to commercial varieties bought in your health food store, unless you know what you are picking. Try wild sages if you are familiar with them and know they haven't been sprayed. For this reason, avoid sage along highways and roads.

To preserve the herb's existence, do not pick wild sage during droughts or pull it up by the roots. The plants are easily recognized by their pungent odor, one reason why fledgling medicine healers and commercial retailers are harvesting it from the wild. Brush sage is more plentiful and is rougher and larger to handle but less endangered. Just dry the sage upside down and then pull leaves off the stems (using gloves), discarding the rest in your compost pile or making a safe outside fire as branches burn like paper.

Brush sage is sold in stores in bundles for smoldering and consequent smoke. These handheld bundles work well outside. Don't use them inside as sparks are certain to burn holes in your carpet unless you have a large fireproof area where the stick can sit and where you don't mind the smoke. Inside, use incense or smolder your sacred sage in bits or in small sticks in a fireproof receptical.

Native Americans used wormwood or sage brush varieties to kill parasites, hence the name. Wormwood essential oil concentrate should be used sparingly, not exceeding recommended doses. The concentrated oil or tincture is toxic and should be kept out of the reach of children and amateur health practitioners.

Because it was available, sage has been used over the years to treat countless ailments and, because of its high oil content, seems to be effective for colds, sore throats and parasites and as a tea, for encouraging sweating and helping digestion. It may also contribute to the health of the sexual glands by clearing congestion of lymph or bodily fluids.

## Juniper

Juniper, like sage, was a versatile and important vegetation to the ancients and remains so to the present. While both juniper and sage are chief smudging herbs, they are far too versatile for only that use. Junipers, cedars, and pines contributed countless gifts to the native peoples. These trees furnished hardy supplies of vitamins and valuable components for medicine. They are clearly one of the outstanding natural wonders of the earth. With them, Indians healed, bathed, worshipped, gave offerings, smudged people and dwellings, and constructed sacred teepees and lodges. Indians burned dried limbs for warmth and spiritual protection, fashioned branches for fences, and used the needles for bedding and smudging ceremonies.

Berries and needles were administered for treating ailments of every kind. The leaves and berries used for healing accounted for cures and the berries and pine nuts contributed food. Juniper needles contain high dosages of vitamin C, which, when drunk, helped supplement the lack of fresh fruit in the winter. Juniper berries contain essential oils, tannin and organic acids. Red Cloud brewed the leaves for drinking and bathing to help his people at the Pine Ridge Indian Reservation. Melvin Gilmore, in *Uses of Plants by the Indians of the Missouri River Region*, notes that Red Cloud found success with this plant during the Asiatic cholera epidemic of 1845–50 and saved some of his people.

Native Americans called juniper "white man's cedar." Confusion of the two species is reflected in the scientific and popular names. Desert white cedar is actually a member of the juniper family (*Juniperus monosperma*), as is Eastern red cedar (*Juniperus virginia*). Both were used in ceremonial smudging. In California, Western red cedar (*thuja occidentalis*) and California incense cedar (*Libocedrus descurrens*) were used for smudging because they were readily available.

If you ask nurseries for accurate labeling, you probably will find as much confusion as there is for "real smudging wood" among shamans. The reason for different viewpoints is that all the names have been used interchangeably at one time or another and there is no difference among varieties for use in smudging ceremonies.

These trees also make wonderful additions to your yard as they provide decorative and esthetic additions to your landscaping. If you live in a dry area, make sure you give the plants extra water, and remember that if you are going to plant one in your yard you want one that will only grow to a size appropriate for the space. You want one that is free of bagworm; check with your plant nursery.

For smudging use, either variety is fine. If you're collecting wood in the forest, choose loose and dried needles, sticks and limbs. Never cut down healthy juniper branches or trees for smudging purposes. Collect the fallen leaves or weak or crowded branches to dry for burning. A large tree in your yard will drop enough needles in the summer or during a dry spell to provide plenty of smudging material. Dried, these are extremely flammable because of their oils, so they should be stored properly. Do not burn your Christmas tree or large, dried branches in an indoor fireplace, as it can start a fire.

Cedar shavings are sold by lumber yards and spiritual stores to use as clearing herbs. Juniper and cedar incense is available, as are oils and candles. These are easy to use indoors and give the air a festive aroma. Use at holidays as well as daily to give you and your home a good sensory experience. Sweet grass, pruned rose bushes and fallen willow sticks make good additions to outdoor smudging and fires.

## PRESERVATION OF JUNIPER

While the traditional red man rarely destroyed the esteemed juniper without need, these trees have been indiscriminately cut down over the years, thereby reducing the supply of their fruit, which is a foodstuff for wild birds and animals. Junipers also provide bird homes and shelter. They traditionally have been used as Christmas trees and today families in certain regions still go out and cut one to decorate for the holidays.

For those desiring a "real tree," junipers can be purchased from nurseries with their roots balled for replanting. These trees can be kept inside in a warm room for several days before Christmas. Once planted, they must be watered frequently for the next few months to establish a root system, or they will die.

These trees offer dignity and protection to your yard and home as they grow. When planting be sure to allow enough space for growth. Large-variety juniper trees, given proper care, grow quickly and within ten years will be wider and taller than an average room. Pick bushy young trees, for they will grow to look similar when aged. The cultivated groundcover varieties are beautiful when used to border driveways or sidewalks and are bagworm-free.

## USING JUNIPER TODAY

The berries are sold in health food stores in various forms by herbal companies. Juniper has diuretic qualities and is used today for assisting sluggish kidneys or bladder problems. It makes a flavorable and nutritious tea. Juniper has stimulating properties and is a healthy replacement for regular tea or coffee. Kidney diseases may be irritated by juniper, so always check with your doctor before treatment of undiagnosed kidney ailments.

### *Juniper berry*

For bloating, backaches, or water retention caused by sluggish kidneys, take several capsules with water. Crush or blend dried berries in a coffee grinder and brew them in water for a tea, one teaspoon of herbal berries to one cup boiling water. Never put herbs in a microwave or boil herbs unless directions specify. If you want to use a microwave, first heat the water in the microwave and then remove it and add the herb to steep. Boil mineral or spring water on the stove before adding the herb.

# 4 Healing Herbs

*They came and gave an herb to me and said: 'With this on earth you shall undertake anything and do it'. It was the day-break-star herb,* the herb of understanding, and they told me to drop it on the earth. I saw it falling far, and when it struck the earth it rooted and grew and flowered, four blossoms on one stem, a blue, a white, a scarlet, and a yellow; and the rays from these streamed upward to the heavens....[22]

In the year 1535 Jacques Cartier, a French explorer, began to lose his crew to scurvy. When his ship remained frozen in the St. Lawrence River for four months, twenty-five men died of this disease, which began with bleeding sores. One sick crew member whose legs rotted limped across the frozen river to seek help from the Indians. He returned cured. Native Americans treated him with a recipe widely believed today to be brewed from a juniper or pine tree. The bark and leaves of the tree boiled into a mixture was applied as a poultice to the wounds and brewed as a tea. Cartier sought out the remedy and saved the rest of his men. That was the first known use of an herbal remedy given by the Indians. We know today scurvy is a result of a vitamin C deficiency (ascorbic acid) in the body.

Certain recently discovered herbal products considered "new," like pycnogenol—a substance made from a French maritime pine bark—perhaps contain ingredients similar to the Great Lakes pines or junipers which cured the French explorers of scurvy. The French sailors had to learn from foreign natives about ingredients from trees like their own which would have prevented the scourge common at sea.

A similar situation exists today. We have the knowledge to prevent many diseases, but people and institutions tend to ignore the obvious and companies like to endorse products that sell. We can use the preventative approach to well-being by eating healthy foods which contain essential nutrients and by using herbs and supplements readily available to all. American bodies are basically starved of essential minerals and need vitamin and nutritional supplements.

Dr. Linus Pauling, a Nobel Prize winner, who recently died in his nineties, had advocated massive doses of vitamin C for years as a preventative health measure. The value of vitamin C has commonly been ignored except by the average person who takes a little mixed vitamin pill every day. It is rarely recommended in a doctor's office, as Dr. Pauling was considered to be eccentric in his beliefs. Vitamin C can be purchased almost everywhere, is inexpensive and can be taken in large doses without any ill effects. Dr. Pauling advocated 10,000 mg a day, took it himself, and outlived all his colleagues.

Cutting down ancient trees in rain forests and wilderness areas to get natural chemical substances like pycnogenol to cure people creates future problems. These areas protect and provide food for the wild life in the region, are esthetically important as nature's gifts and are crucial to our health. The trees preserve the ozone layer so we can go out in the sun without getting dangerous radiation. Wooded areas emit gasses which are critical to the ecological balance of the earth's atmosphere. The earth's vegetation preserves stable climatic conditions, preventing a dangerous melting of the ice caps, which could tilt our planet's axis.

Commonly known health habits like eating fruits and vegetables and using natural remedies from plants reduce health problems. If we ate better diets and improved our thoughts and actions to help ourselves and others, the body wouldn't need unusual products to help prevent collapse of an organ or the immune system. The great forests can then be tapped conservatively for the supply of exotic herbal plants for those in need.

Plant products like grapefruit seed extract are readily available. Grapefruit seeds contain ingredients known to protect against cancer-causing free radicals in the body. Grapefruit seed extract has also been "discovered" to be a natural preservative for cosmetics and foods and to cause few of the detrimental side effects caused by the nitrates and sulfates common in packaged fresh food and produce. Using this easily extracted ingredient from grapefruit will encourage planting trees instead of cutting down forests and, at the same time, provide a natural, safe preservative.

Modern analysis of the chemical composition of plants documents their proper use by the Indians. Synthetic duplication of compounds found in them accounts for numerous over-the-counter and prescriptive medicines. Diazepam, known by the trade name Valium, was synthesized from components of the native herb valerian and became one of the overprescribed drugs of the twentieth century. Valium overdoses accounted for thousands of emergency room visits, addictions, and deaths during the decades it was in vogue with doctors.

It is easier to write a prescription for "nerves" than to take the time to ask about problems in the person's life. Sometimes the patients are at fault, since they will use every means possible to get doctors to prescribe pills rather than make changes in themselves or their environment.

Natural compounds can be chemically duplicated in the laboratory. But although synthetic products are stronger and more effective in emergencies, they are easily misused. Pharmaceutical drugs lack certain enzymes and elements needed for optimum health. Today, people treat physical symptoms in isolation, disregarding the nutritional needs of the body. For example, a headache is killed with painkillers; no attempt is made to discover and cure the underlying cause of the headache, which is only a symptom of a problem in the mind or body. Curing and treating symptoms is known as allopathic medicine and is the type practiced by our established medical system.

Contemporary allopathic medicine has saved many lives and is necessary in our hectic and increasingly unhealthy environment. For example, miracle surgeries after accidents and to preserve and lengthen life spans through organ transplants are wonders of contemporary medicine that provide hope and healing. Antibiotics are lifesavers and one of the modern miracles of scientific drug discovery. When the body's immune system has deteriorated to a certain critical point, drug compounds and unusual procedures are necessary to sustain life.

The overuse of prescription drugs, however, is one of the chief causes of illness and death in the elderly. The drugs, often working against each other, clog the body, making it harder for the natural healing process to take place.

No physician worth his salt should insist on synthetic drugs for his patient, if the person being treated prefers herbs and natural medications instead. Synthetic drugs kill more people than herbs do. Unfortunately, we never hear about such matters unless they appear in some kind of statistical form—'An Estimated 27,900 Americans Die Every Year from Prescription Drugs!'—as a column 'filler.'... But let one or two persons die from the misuse of herbs and immediately the rare tragedy is screamed all over the front page in bold headlines....[23]

Allopathic doctors attempt to cure cancer caused by toxic overload by giving the body even more chemicals. Chemotherapy and radiation using poisonous substances kill healthy tissue as well as cancers.

Despite billions of dollars spent in research, little progress has been accomplished in curing cancer with the exception of a few select types of cancers using ingredients extracted from plants! This herb, *Vinca rosa,* a relative of the periwinkle plant, contains alkaloids, which are used to create one of the few documented powerful drugs found to arrest or "cure" certain leukemias and lymphomas.

The composition of the alkaloids arrests cancer cell multiplication by binding them to a protein found in the cells. This progress in the cure or remission of these cancers appears to be about the only actual headway in curing cancer after millions and millions of dollars spent and time wasted.

While early detection isn't a cure, progress has been made in sophisticated machines and tests which show early development of cancerous or diseased tissue.

In past years, good health knowledge was unknown. Today there is more health information available than a person can read. It is necessary to focus on your own health situation and take action yourself. If you have cancer or a serious disease, it is best to study your own health situation. Buy a physician's *Merck Manual* (published by Merck Sharp & Dohme Research Laboratories), talk to naturopathic doctors, read natural healing books, converse with your conventional medical doctor, and decide for yourself what you want to do.

Follow the above advice so you can have the best of both worlds (allopathic and naturopathic) in attacking your disease. If you are taking prescription medicine for any health problem, buy yourself a *Physician's Desk Reference,* known as the PDR, published by Medical Economics, and talk to your doctor about the drugs you are taking.

To prevent the occurrence of illnesses, start a natural health program as suggested in this book. Continue to keep current by learning all you can.

## Using Nature's Herbs

Herbs, like all organic matter, offer specific vitamins, enzymes, minerals and other beneficial effects yet to be discovered. Each plant used in healing has its own unique chemical atomic composition: a combination of molecules consisting of a particular arrangement of electrons revolving about a nucleus containing protons and neutrons.

Specific herbs and plants have vibrational levels attributed to their unique organic compounds and are drawn magnetically to similar elements. Certain herbs have an affinity or attraction to certain parts of the body and tissues and contribute nutrients and healing properties to that area or organ. This is one of the principles, besides nutrients and resultant effects, that determine what herb is good or beneficial for which part of the body. For example, nervines like valerian are so named because they heal the nerves. Dandelion is a natural cleanser for the liver.

Deep sea fish vary in their mineral content. Shrimp naturally attract traces of arsenic, a mineral found in the ocean and in small quantities in the body. Overeating shrimp can make you feel queasy from ingesting too much arsenic at once. In addition, natural shrimp breeding grounds are ocean shelf-beds which may be contaminated by industrial waste dumping grounds. Commercially cultivated shrimp farms are numerous today. Thousands of harvestable shrimp are jammed into overcrowded spaces with their own excrement and rotting leftover feed. To combat disease, they are overdosed with pesticides and antibiotics. Several years later, the land used is poisoned and barren. For your best bet for safe shrimp, ask for "turtle-safe" shrimp at your market. This will help ensure endangered sea turtles have been released from nets and that the shrimp have been caught at sea (hopefully in the purest water). One hopes all shellfish (they are scavengers) will have healthy environments in the future.

Americans aren't easily treated with herbal compounds. Their bodies are on chemical overload from pesticides, insecticides, food preservatives, toxic cleaning agents and work-related environmental contaminants. Add to that individual weaknesses in the body brought on by a high-stress environment and increasingly weak genetic constitutions resulting from generations of eating overprocessed foods that provide poor mineral intake and starve glands and organs. The result is the diminished effectiveness of any healing agent, including herbal remedies. For example, pressure from an impacted colon and a lack of natural hormone production reduce the effectiveness of the herb black cohosh on the uterus, which is a natural relaxant for cramping of the female organs.

The strength of any herb will depend on nutrients present in the soil, the effectiveness of preservation techniques, whether the herb was sprayed or radiated, and, perhaps, whether it was picked at the right time. The results of an herb's healing properties vary widely by individual and are affected by the individual's physical and mental health.

If there were one single deficit in American diets that contributes to countless disease states it would be a lack of minerals. Minerals are found in vegetables and plants and are highly concentrated in the sea, where mineral content has been leached from the land and concentrated in the water. These minerals are assimilated into fish and sea plants such as seaweed. People with sufficient income and without next-door, fast-food restaurants such as may be found in areas of Japan, do not suffer from mineral deficiencies. In the United States, Hawaiians have the longest life span, due to the minerals in the soil of the island and the seafood eaten.

Laboratory-designed processed foods often lack the natural minerals needed to feed vital glands and organs. The processing not only cheats you of natural enzymes, but adds toxins and makes the body work harder. These factors create a suppressed immune system that lacks the nutritional strength to fight disease. Vital endocrine, glandular and blood-cell deficiencies result. Poor immune systems have set the stage for new immune disorders such as AIDS.

Native Americans healed faster than Europeans using herbal remedies because they were better nourished and believed in the spiritual sacredness of their environment and their bodies. Native Americans believed animals and plants were nourishing and curing gifts from their god. Healing yourself requires more than taking an herb or treating a physical symptom. Today, countless Americans don't seem to care what they do to their bodies. Diets contain too few minerals and too much fat and sugar. There is little interest in purging and cleansing the body for either spiritual or physical reasons. Optimum health requires a certain thinking or mind-set, a belief in the sacredness of your own body: *The Body is the temple of your Soul.*

# Using Native American Wonder Herbs

## Echinacea

(ECHINACEA ANGUSTIFOLIA)

Commonly known as purple coneflower, this beautiful flowering plant used to blanket entire fields of the American plains and still grows everywhere herbal companies haven't overpicked it. Its wonder-drug reputation threatens its existence in the wild. For good reason, the Indians used it for everything. It contains natural antibiotic qualities and heals infections. It was used as an antidote for poisonous insects and snakebites and to heal earaches in children and distemper in horses.

Echinacea is commonly stocked in health food sections and stores and contemporary naturopaths use it in the place of antibiotics. In case of severe infection, you should consult your medical doctor, as herbs may not work quickly enough for safety's sake. Use echinacea when you are treating colds, viruses, and minor skin irritations or infections. Using it for minor problems (instead of taking an antibiotic) helps keep your body from becoming immune to prescription antibiotics when you really need them!

This herb like others works better in combination. For a cold or flu, use it with vitamin C, goldenseal, wild yam, raspberry tea and myrrh gum tincture. Myrrh is an Old World herb used in biblical times as a drug and for its perfume. The condensed myrrh sold in tincture form will not smell and taste anything like perfume. It is quite strong and should only be used as directed on the bottle and when you are sick. It may be one of the few herbal drugs that kills viruses. When the commercial companies "discover" its virtues, watch for the price to skyrocket.

## Goldenseal
### (HYDRASTIS CANADENSIS)

This herb is currently almost extinct in the wild but, fortunately, is cultivated commercially. The Indians used it to treat battle wounds and serious contagious venereal diseases brought from Europe. Goldenseal has an affinity for mucous membranes and is used today to treat infections of the teeth and gums, tonsillitis, chronic intestinal disorders, and skin problems. It is another miracle herb containing alkaloids, which means it is strong and powerful and should be used only when needed. Combined with myrrh gum tincture, it is a powerful antiseptic agent which can be used when traveling in places where doctors are not available.

## Burdock
### (ARCTIUM LAPPA)

The original burdock variety (*Arctium minus*), used by the Cherokee Indians for swollen and ulcerated leg wounds,[24] was replaced in herbal arsenals by the *lappa* species from Europe. According to Melvin Gilmore, it grows wild along old traffic routes used by early military and civilian travelers:

> It has been adopted by the Indians for medicinal use. White Horse, of the Omaha, gave information...obtained from the Oto, of a decoction of the root being used as a remedy for pleurisy.[25]

The Russians also recognize it as a diaphoretic and use it to treat water retention, to provoke sweating, to remove toxins and for tissue cleansing.

Burdock is also recognized as a valuable blood and lymph-gland cleanser. Another cleanser for mucous membranes, this valuable herb is also a demulcent, which means it soothes tender skin and membranes by relieving inflammation. Skin eruptions, fever blisters, genital or intestinal irritations and any other mucous membrane problem may be helped. John Heinerman, in *Science of Herbal Medicine*, states that burdock breaks up waste material in the bloodstream so it can be eliminated through the kidneys and is therefore helpful for arthritis.

Any part of the plant can be used safely. In countries that need it, it is used as a food. For the rest of us, capsules bought at health-food stores can be swallowed or broken apart and used externally on the skin. For naturalists, your dog may help you find it in the wild by picking up burrs on its coat. Combine burdock with an equal amount of golden seal for a stronger antiseptic but less soothing mixture.

## Chaparral
(LARREA DIVARICATA)

Chaparral, a creosote bush, belongs to a large varied group of southwestern plants. It is an antiseptic herb which has been used for everything and is not associated with a cure for any particular disorder except one. As reported by Alma Hutchens:

> Indians of the south-western areas used the plant as varied symptoms prevailed...in October 1967, after three previous surgically removed growths, an eighty-five-year-old man refused medical treatment on the...fourth-recurrent growth, documented as malignant melanoma, in favour of 'Chaparral tea', an old Indian remedy. Of this tea he drank 2–3 cups a day. In September 1968 he was re-examined at the Medical Centre, Utah, U.S.A., which found that the growth had decreased from the size of a large lemon to that of a dime. No other medication was used.... In eleven months he gained a needed 25 lb., with improvements in general health....[26]

Today chaparral is used as mentioned and as an antiseptic for infection. It is also sold in combination herbal formulas which cannot be labelled to state that they treat any particular disorder such as cancer. The only legally recognized cancer treatments are chemotherapy and radiation; it is against the law to advertise a natural herb or formula as potentially helpful. Cancer patients with systemic lymph-gland involvement have only a small chance of living more than five years. Research has not shown that either radiation or chemotherapy is a cure when cancer has spread to other areas of the body. These patients should be free to choose any method they wish to remove the cancer. Those who survive in spite of the odds have been found to be optimists who have used a variety of conventional and alternative health practices. Mind-set was found to be more important than the treatment used!

## Barberry
(BERBERIS VULGARIS)

## Oregon Grape Root
(BERBERIS AQUIFOLIUM)

Over one hundred species of shrubs make up the family of Berberidaceae, of which these two species are members. They are similar in composition and characteristics. Both are excellent antiseptics, blood thinners, and tonics for the body. Like the above-mentioned herbs in this category, the Indians used them externally for numerous healings of wounds and abrasions and for treating chronic diseases internally. They cleanse the liver and gall bladder by increasing the production of bile, and the kidneys by cleansing the blood. The production of bile has a laxative effect and a stimulating effect on the thyroid gland.[27] Oregon grape root is sometimes combined with antispasmodics like wild yam, valerian and black cohosh to cleanse while relaxing the organs.

## Black Cohosh
### (Cimicifuga racemosa)

Black cohosh, known by Native Americans as snakeroot, was used by the Indians for snake bite. Interestingly, it is known today to reduce high blood pressure, an effect which, one would assume, would reduce the speed at which snake poison circulates in the body. In addition to its value as a treatment for snake bite, it was used primarily by the Indians for helping women in childbirth and with menstruation difficulties, as it helps subdue spasms. It often went by the name squawroot.

Black cohosh is included in this section, instead of in the herbal nervine list at the end of this chapter, as it is more than just an antispasmodic: it is an "all-around" wonder herb. Rather strong, it will produce nausea or headaches if used in high doses. Since individual tolerances vary, start with one capsule or one-half dropper of tincture and increase as tolerated to two or three times that amount daily or as needed.

Today black cohosh is used to treat high blood pressure, asthma, respiratory infections like bronchitis, spastic conditions in the colon and duodenum and nervous conditions. Take it in combination with mullein to treat asthma and with other antispasmodic nervines like lobelia, valerian or skullcap as a relaxant. Reduce the quantity when you combine it with other nervines.

## Saint John's-wort
### (Hypericum perforatum)

Saint John's-wort, also an antispastic nervine, is included in this section due to its unique constituent, hypericin, which acts as an anti-depressant. Even though research demonstrated fifty years ago that it was an antidepressant and it was listed in the Merck Manual for doctors, only recently has it begun to be utilized, in place of prescription antidepressants, by people finding out about it and purchasing it over the counter. Saint John's-wort is useful for menstrual cramps, nervousness, insomnia, acne, and liver cleansing.

Like the prescriptive antidepressants, it needs to be taken regularly before effects are noticed. Follow the instructions on the bottle and vary dosage to experiment with your energy level. Remember though, the mind cannot be "cured" if your depression is caused by repressed anger or disappointment, the subject of the next section, which discusses the mind's influence on the body's physical well-being: *The Mind is the temple of your Spirit.*

## Heal the Mind

Thought is energy and what the mind believes changes the cellular structure of the body. Desire is the fuel that increases the intensity of the mind energy to accomplish the wish. With a mind-set for healing, the immune system receives an extra boost.

Have you ever noticed that you are more likely to be sick after performing a task you didn't want to do? Conversely, you can be tired and join in a strenuous fun activity and end up feeling better than you did before.

Negative energy from either yourself or the environment depresses the immune system and makes it difficult for spiritual, mental or herbal remedies to work. Using a natural product in combination with a desire to heal the body actually raises the immune capacity of the body, increasing the vibrational and spiritual level of the body at the same time.

Becoming healthier mentally requires a threefold process:

1. Improve your physical health through better habits and nutrition.
2. Establish a mind-set which feels and knows you to be a sacred person; believe in you; picture yourself perfect in

mind and body.

3. Be your unique self; bring fun into your life by "following your bliss."

The mental-emotional component is ignored today despite volumes of research demonstrating the importance of mind-set: at least seventy-five percent of the time, illnesses are related to problems outside the physical realm. All the medicines in the world won't cure a person who has lost the desire to live. What seemed to some to be paganistic rituals by superstitious witch doctors were important healing processes because they gave the patient hope that someone cared and was willing to stay with them, and also created trust in the magic of the shaman to perform the cure.

Studies indicate the importance of doctor-client relationships and trust in the caretaker. This factor is recognized today in Indian hospitals where traditional medicine men and women may work together with contemporary doctors. Again, the holistic approach is preferred.

To help heal yourself both physically and mentally, use natural herbal nervines which:

1. Actually help heal the nervous system instead of covering up symptoms or dulling the brain, and
2. Help relax and calm the mind for a better attitude about yourself and your life.

Contemporary society promotes the tension and stress that account for a large percentage of mental and physical problems. With a plethora of wonderful nervines available at health-food stores and specialty stores and, increasingly, in drugstores and grocery stores, there is no reason not to try these herbal remedies. While they are becoming more expensive as demand develops, they are still inexpensive compared to prescription drugs. Experiment with the nervines singularly and in combination until you find one remedy which fits your body chemistry the best.

Also try also the wonderful flower essences for nervous problems. One example is the Bach Flower Essences sold in health-food stores. Experiment for results and write down findings. One of the mistakes people make is taking a remedy, finding relief, going on with their routine, forgetting what helped them the last time they felt that way, and then forgetting to use it later when the problem returns!

Flower essences can be used as often as you like. They aren't a drug. Try different flower essence brands and gem therapy until you find your favorite.

## Healing Your Nerves with Herbs

### Valerian
(VALERIANA OFFICINALIS)

Valium, a valuable sedative in surgical procedures and at one time a widely overprescribed drug, was derived by synthetically duplicating chemical elements from the herb valerian. While valium has since earned a bad reputation, it still is a valuable surgical drug used in countless out-patient operations to temporarily render the person unaware of pain as the doctors work on the body.

Valerian is a multifaceted healer that was used by Native Americans for alleviating nervous symptoms and for easing the pain of swollen joints. Its root was ground into flour to eat in times of famine.

It is indigenous to countries with low lying meadows and wet marshes or riverbanks. It is easily grown in a backyard garden. Cats and rats are said to be as attracted to valerian root as they are to another nervine, catnip. Valerian mixes well with other nervines like catnip, skullcap, yellow lady's slipper or a little lobelia to make a mixture to help you sleep, relax, or be less anxious.

The tincture is easiest to use. Take one dropperful of valerian tincture three or four times a day as needed. Double as an emergency dose for spasms or cramps. It is also available in capsule form. Follow the directions on the label. Do not use valerian daily or indiscriminately. As with all drug treatments, do not use it in place of dealing with the problem causing the nervousness.

While those who grow valerian may have enough root to place in a hot bath, for those that purchase it, it is too precious to waste. Valerian may be drunk as a tea; pour boiling water over several teaspoons of root until infused.

Valerian, as all nervines, has a strong taste and smell. While the herb acts as a relaxant in normal doses for humans, cats become giddy and excited, perhaps due to their small size or different brain systems. For cats, it is an aphrodisiac! For humans, these relaxants may have the opposite effect, unless you are the obsessive-compulsive type who needs to be less uptight. Read on.

## Skullcap
(SCUTELLARIA LATERIFLORA)

Another indigenous nervine is skullcap, an antispasmodic and relaxant. Like its friend valerian, it grows in damp places all across the United States.

Skullcap helps promote sleep, reduces agitation, and helps heal frayed nerves. Certain tribes used it in rituals to promote menstruation, to treat other female problems such as cramping, and as an aid in breast feeding.

Like other nervines, it soothes a nervous heart. Note that all heart palpitations or similar problems should be first checked by a physician.

Those who are concerned about their sex drive should be

aware that the old literature claims nervines will reduce "undue sexual desire"! I guess one has to decide what kind of "tension" one wants and when one wants it. However, since constitutions vary, perhaps nervous personalities might benefit from small doses. Depressive personalities probably won't. Again, try the nervines and see!

## Wild Lettuce
(LACTUCA SPECIES)

A natural nervine, wild lettuce was used by various Indian tribes to treat female disorders and to help with childbirth and breast feeding. A natural sedative, it may have been used in ritual for female "detoxification": to release contamination from menstruation (blood was thought to interfere with the power of the medicine rituals).

Iceberg lettuce, the favorite with Americans, has the fewest minerals and vitamins of all the green leafy vegetables, but has small quantities of sedative-type characteristics. Unfortunately for those liking big, heavy meals, it is thought by some to slow down, and thus interfere with, digestion! Bad news for those steak and potato eaters who thought they were eating enough vegetables with a couple of leaves of iceberg lettuce!

## Wild Onions
(ALLIUM MUTABILE)

Onions were eaten raw, boiled in stews and fried. They have both antiseptic and decongestant qualities. They aid in digestion, expel worms and kill bacterial and fungus infections. Onion poultices were used to heal battle wounds and skin infections. Both onions and garlic lower blood pressure. Some people believe onions produce a drowsy feeling similar to taking a nervine or sedative.

Onions when worn, like garlic, were thought to provide protection due to their volatile oils. In *Indian Herbalogy of North*

*America,* Alma Hutchens points out that crushed onion or garlic will kill a bacteria culture in a few minutes when placed next to it. During the Middle Ages, or "vampire season," perhaps the wearing of garlic around the neck actually kept away bacterial invasions or other nasty critters.

## Catnip
(NEPETA CATARIA)

Catnip, which is usually associated with cats, grows wild all over America. It is one of the few herbs recommended by physicians for babies, including Humbart Santillo, N.D., author of *Natural Healing with Herbs.* In doses of one tablespoon per one pint of boiling water (steep covered until body temperature), it can be used as a bowel injection for babies with colic or added to baby formula to ease pain. Use in crisis situations only. Adult dosages are three tablespoons per one pint of boiling water; again, don't boil, just steep until body temperature.Use all herbal formulas in moderation and only when needed.

## Lady's Slipper
(CYPRIPEDIUM VARIETIES)

Lady's slipper was used like valerian, which is a distantly related species, for nervous conditions in women and children, especially by Indians in the eastern part of the United States like the Cherokee and Ojibwas. The herb, used for menstrual cramps, insomnia and hysteria, is both a sedative and an antispasmodic. Adopted by early white doctors (before pharmaceutical companies), it found its way into popular use for men as well.

Steep several teaspoons in about twelve ounces of water longer than ordinary (up to an hour). The tincture is stronger but easier to use. Take up to thirty drops a day as needed. Combine with lobelia and skullcap for increased relief from cramping or nervous attacks.

# How to Reduce Tension Situations

Medicine healers in tribes used the whole family and neighbors in healing for emotional problems related to interpersonal interactions. Dreams were analyzed when the emotional crisis was intrinsic. Today, if you can't afford therapy and want to improve your situation, take the initiative to discover and make changes within yourself. The following exercise will help you take crucial steps toward having the life you deserve.

List the situations in which you find yourself feeling:

Powerless_____

_____

Unhappy _____

_____

Angry_____

_____

Sad _____

_____

Tense_____

_____

Anxious _____

_____

Embarrassed _____

_____

Inadequate_____

_____

Include situations from your past and present that bring these feelings to memory. Are there recurring themes? Is there a common thread that gives you clues to the reason for the problem? For each situation listed, write them out on paper.

## CHECKLIST

1. Are you trying to control other people?

___

2. Is your pride or ego involved?

___

3. Are you afraid of being hurt emotionally?

___

4. Do you avoiding making decisions?

___

5. Do materialistic concerns take precedence over people?

___

6. Are you angry or resentful?

___

7. Do you see everything as black or white?

___

8. Are you being deceitful or having to lie?

___

9. Are you jealous or suspicious?

___

10. Are you doing what you want to do in life?

___

Check any question that applies to you and list beside it what situations made you feel that way. *Determine the specific life event where you find yourself feeling your worst. Then state the first most important single action you must do to correct this negative situation.* Write down the first step you have to take to change from a nervous state to a happier one.

The situation where I feel the worst is

_____

What I must do to take action on this problem is

_____

Changing old negative habits and patterns is difficult, but if you truly want with all your heart to change your life, you must stick to whatever action is needed and follow through regardless of what excuses you can come up with not to.

After following through on the first most important single thing to do, the second step, the action needed to solve the problem, is taken. If you are sincere and truly striving for a better life with no ill intent to others you will be assisted from higher powers to succeed.

Now that you've attacked your worst stresses, the intent to change your life will begin to transform the physical/mental/spiritual cellular makeup of your body. We possess primordial memory traces in our bodies, cells and genes from the previous experiences of our ancestors and, some believe, our past lives. In addition, the experiences throughout our life impact our current skeletal/muscular and mental/emotional cellular structure.

One important hint to reducing stress is to avoid vacillating about decisions. *Learn to say Yes-Yes or No-No to every situation and then stick to it.* Give yourself several opportunities to assess the situation, make your decision and stay with it until the situation in which you are "stuck" no longer exists. Do not deviate from your goal to conquer the most important change you need to make in your life. It will happen if you really want to change. Use your herbal formulas to assist you and watch the positive changes that will take place in your life. Good luck!

# 5 Plants as Herbs

By far the most important of the agricultural rituals was the Corn Dance. A Franciscan friar, writing in the seventeenth century, observed that:

> If you look closely at the Indians, you will see that everything they say and do is connected with corn. They practically make a god of it. They indulge in so much conjuring and fussing about in their corn fields that they...behave as if the only aim in life was to produce a crop of corn.[28]

For centuries, agricultural tribes celebrated to honor the corn crop, naming rituals after the being: Green Corn (planting), Maiden Corn (immature corn), Mother Corn (mature corn harvest). Today, southwestern Pueblos, such as the Santa Domingo Indians in New Mexico, continue to celebrate ceremonially with the Corn Dance. In the spring, a four-day period of community dancing followed by a four-day period of fasting and prayer in homes are rites for favorable planting. The next corn dance, to thank the young corn crop known in some Pueblos as Maiden Corn, is in August. This costumed and important event is well-attended by surrounding Pueblos and open to tourists at certain times. The fall ceremony honors the harvest of the mature corn.

Young girls weren't considered marriageable until they proved their skill at making corn tortillas. Young Navajo girls poured cornmeal into fireplace ashes to make a tortilla of perfect shape and flavor. To make flat bread, Hopi girls poured corn flour, soaked in lime water to soften its texture, onto hot, greased stones.

Corn was part of the coming-of-age rites and marriage preparation ceremonies for young women. Corn rituals, considered a symbol of fertility, assured the woman would have children, be able to cook and nourish her family, and be a good wife. The Pawnee mother routinely offered kernels of corn to the altar.

> Before they began their meal, White Woman made an offering of corn at the west. She took some kernels of corn in a spoon from Victory Call's bowl and offered them to the nose of the buffalo skull that rested on the altar there. Out of delicacy, she did not offer corn to the sacred ears in the bundle....[29]

Corn may be the first crop cultivated in North America by Native Americans. Pollen analysis in soils reveals wild corn as early as 80000 B.C.! The earliest evidence of corn planting dating from 3000 B.C. was found in New Mexico. The red kidney bean showed up in the same area several thousand years before the arrival of the Europeans.[30]

Harold Driver points out that by the arrival of de Soto in the mid-1500s, large quantities of maize (corn), beans, squashes, pumpkins, and sunflowers grew in the Mississippi valley. Besides huge fields of crops, de Soto found large temples and palace mounds, and "witnessed the arrival of male and female chiefs on litters carried on the shoulders of commoners."[31]

Anthropological researcher and herbalist John Heinerman reported that southwestern excavations by anthropologists Vaughn Bryant and Glenna Dean showed high concentrations of pollen from willow, desert sage, greasewood, false-mallow, parsley, Mormon tea (ephedra), and various grasses, including domesticated Indian corn. The importance of pollen (indicating flowers and fruits) in the diet of original Native Americans caused these researchers to label them the flower people.[32]

As rice is to Asians, and wheat now is to the majority of Americans, corn was to the Indians. Today, the United States still produces more corn than all other countries combined. Iowa and Illinois are the two main states for corn production.

Corn, a true grain like barley, rice and rye, is native to the Americas (wheat, barley and rice originated in Europe/Asia). The corn kernels are the large seeds of the plant, the stalk like a giant blade of grass. When the Bermuda grass plant goes to seed, it is a miniature of the mature corn plant ready to harvest. There are varieties of corn in South America, with cobs three or four feet high on a stalk the height of a tree.

Indians cultivated hybrid varieties of corn long before the arrival of colonists. When he arrived in the Americas, Columbus reported seeing cornfields eighteen miles long. He took dried seed corn back to Europe where it began to be cultivated.

The first Native Americans helped the early settlers to grow corn. Every schoolchild knows the Indians used fish or other organic products to help fertilize the soil before planting the corn. Native Americans cultivated different varieties of corn, although regional preferences and climates influenced choices. The mature cornstalk produces tassels on top of the plant. The pollen from these tassels united with the corn silk to produce corn. By hand-pollinating the plants, the Indian created hybrids.

Flint corn was the variety planted in the Northeast, as it grew in the harsh New England climate. Flint corn dried hard and required stones to grind, but lasted indefinitely, thereby assuring food stockpiles. Today it is used commercially as a feed for livestock.

Dent corn, grown by Indians in the southeastern United States, was so named because the middle of the kernel sank in when dried. In the Southwest, flour corn, which is softer, was preferred for the preparation of flat breads like tortillas. This flat corn bread was cooked until dried (like a corn chip today), or the corn was ground into flour to be preserved for future eating. An older variety of sweet corn, grown for centuries, may have been consumed by tribes at peak harvest, except in times of plenty when it was stored. Sweet-corn varieties bought at the grocery store today are still popular whether fresh, canned or frozen.

All harvested corn was either cooked on the husks, and then scraped and dried, or dried on the stalk. Corn dried on the cob required longer soaking and cooking time but stored longer. The harder the corn variety, the safer it was from molds and wild creatures. Today's hybrid corn has a tough outer layer for easier shipping, but is harder to digest. Eating corn tortillas or corn mush (polenta) is superior for obtaining nutrients and ease of digestion.

Corn, with about twelve percent protein, was combined with beans (about twenty-five percent protein) to balance the chemical protein deficiencies in each. Corn was mixed with beans or other vegetables in stews, or eaten as a bread. Adding wild greens, fruit, nuts, and meat, when available, provided an almost perfect diet. Today, vegetarians know corn combined with beans make a complete protein in a meatless meal.

Soaking cornmeal in lime water softened it for tortillas. Research indicates the lime provides the body with a powerful calcium supply for good teeth and bones. Indian and Mexican children on the native diet, considered to be living in poor socioeconomic conditions, have teeth far superior to those of other children. The need for braces in upper-income families results from the lack of proper nutrients in their diet, one consequence of giving in to demands for advertised sugar cereals and junk food.

Various well-meaning nutritionists, believing they know more about nutrition than their Indian or Mexican friends, have tried to convert these people from their standard diet. The truth is that the natural Native American and Mexican diet, still eaten by hundreds of thousands of people, is highly nutritious. Corn, beans, onions, avocados, tomatoes, red and green peppers, cilantro (Mexican parsley), nuts, honey and dried fruit, combined with custards, eggs, meat or chicken, provide a more balanced diet than the average American's. Seafood or supplements to provide iodine and minerals are needed for those living inland.

The Cherokee, noted for their good looks, tall stature and intelligence, originated along the southeastern coast of the United States where seafood (and consequently minerals from the sea) was available. The same characteristics were true of the northeastern tribes like the Iroquois, whose national constitution was an important source for the writing of the American Declaration of Independence. Also nutritious were the diets of the Indians in tropical climates, where fruit, endless varieties of plants, seafood and interesting game like monkeys, lizards and large grubs were available.

Squashes and pumpkins provided the mainstay of the vegetable crop. Roasted pumpkin seeds provided a treat known as *pipitas*. Dried corn, pumpkin and winter squashes were hidden by agricultural tribes in case of a raid from the nomadic Indian tribes wanting to supplement their meat diet during the winter.

European settlers found the vegetables grown by the Indians to be colorful and tasty. Pumpkin was scraped, dried and braided into "fast food" snacks to be easily carried and eaten on demand. Corn flour mixed with honey or maple sugar became a prized winter dessert. Dried fruit and berries lasted until spring.

A combination of dried fruit and meat made *pemmican*, which was easily carried on long journeys or through the winter. Food dried by heat contains all the natural minerals and vitamins it has when fresh.

Melons of various shapes and colors delighted palates in the summer. Flowers from squash and melon plants were prized for flavoring stews. All the edible flowers, and the fruit parts of vegetables and plants, were eaten. In southern Texas, large concentrations of pollen from flowers and seeds were found in Indian ruins dating from 800 B.C. to 500 A.D. The pollen found was derived from yucca, agave, cactus, sotol and mesquite.[33]

Wild foods added important minerals and supplemented farmed foodstuffs. Bone analysis of Prairie Indians showed that those who supplemented their diet with wild foods were healthier than those who ate only cultivated foods.[34] Two of the valuable foods picked from the wild which stored well over the winter were wild potatoes (*Glycine apios*) and black-eyed peas. During their first winter in New England, the Pilgrims are thought to have survived by eating wild potatoes given to them by the Indians.

After the Indians saved the lives of the Pilgrims by showing them how to survive on the potato, in 1654 the settlers passed a typical law that forbade the Indians from digging these tubers on "English Land." For a first offense a Native American was liable to be jailed, and for the second, whipping was the reward.[35]

Exacerbating the political problem was the division of Indian tribes for and against the British Empire during the American revolution. The great Iroquois Confederacy divided itself oversupport for the British and the American colonists. The Oneida helped keep General Washington's soldiers from starving at Valley Forge by giving them hundreds of bushels of corn. Washington's troops then burned the Senecas' homes, orchards and cattle, resulting in massive starvation. The Seneca, a member of the Iroquois Confederacy, fought on the side of the British. After the War of Independence, the Oneida, who had helped General Washington, found their land reduced from six million acres to thirty-two! Historically, Native American tribes who split their loyalty to help opposing enemies contributed to the downfall of their own people.

The Indian potato (*Solanum tuberosum*), now known as the Irish potato, was native to the Americas. Word of the value of this plant spread quickly among the arriving settlers, and as early as 1635 it was taken to Europe and cultivated.

Interestingly, the Irish adopted the potato as their main crop in place of rye and wheat. This change eventually resulted in disaster when the potato crops failed and millions starved. When the English refused to help, thousands of Irish were shipped to America. Those that didn't die of starvation or disease on the ships joined the Indians and Blacks as the downtrodden groups of the 1850s. Countless thousands of Americans have mixed Indian-Irish bloodlines from intermarriage as the poor, rural Irish moved into Indian territories. Ironically, the potato, which provided an Indian food supply for years, brought the Irish back to the people and land where it originated.

## Wild Foods and Herbs

Unknown to the average "city slicker," hundreds of varieties of valuable herbal plants still grow wild in North America and in residential yards. The infamous dandelion, and other weeds like mullein, yarrow, pokeweed and lamb's-quarter, are sprayed with herbicide. Herbs in demand like echinacea, which used to flower entire prairies, are threatened with extinction as company herb pickers try to supply demands for this free natural antibiotic.

Spring greens, known to the Indians and early rural settlers, were believed to clear the blood and revitalize the system after the paucity of fresh foods available in the winter. Native American women gathered all the winter greens they could find and added them to the corn and bean stew. Greens like pokeweed, wild lettuce, dandelion, lamb's-quarter, milkweed pods, wild onions and any edible flower or green were gathered and cooked together. Supplies of wild onions, garlic and other "weeds" were assured by cultivation by Native Americans.

Today, the greens and herbs mentioned above are known to be blood cleansers and to add valuable minerals to the diet. Other herbal blood and lymph-gland cleansers are burdock, alfalfa, chickweed, yellow dock, sarsaparilla, chaparral, and red clover. They can be purchased in capsule or dried leaf form and are used to help combat disease. Greens eaten regularly as a preventative measure to stave off disease can be supplemented with stronger cleansing herbs to combat specific health problems.

It is easy, nutritious and tasty to cook greens bought at your store. Greens such as beet greens, kale, mustard, collard greens and spinach are available all year round, and not eaten enough for health's sake. Rinse the greens, toss them in a skillet (still wet) and cook a few minutes until tender. Southerners flavor their greens with ham or bacon, and usually overcook them.

Rural Indians with their own land and farmers still eat greens, corn bread and beans on a regular basis. They go out in their backyards to pick pokeweed greens for supper. If a friendly farmer offers you some pokeweed, please know that these greens have to be cooked—they cannot be served raw. Country people from pioneer stock often live to be ninety-years old.

Data collected by excavation of various sites inhabited by Native Americans in fertile areas like the lower Illinois valley suggest they used the following herbs and plants for medicinal or foodstuffs: tumbleweed, hops, pink weed, watercress, butterfly weed, American lotus, mayapple, prairie clover, dewberry, amaranth, cleavers, ragweed, milkweed, love grass, wild strawberry, spikenard, columbine, marsh elder, yellow oxalis, sedge, roose foot, solomon's seal, cinquefoil, cocklebur, jimson (locoweed), lamb's-quarter, pokeweed, chickweed, violet, mustard, mint and duck potato.[36]

Nuts grown in the area include acorn, hickory, hazel, and black walnut. Included among trees whose inside bark is edible are silver maple, green ash and slippery elm. Fruits from the region include plums, grapes, hackberries and wild persimmons. When they were available, Native Americans ate sunflower seeds (which are fifty-five percent protein), pumpkin seeds, pinon nuts and any edible acorn or nut.

## Nature's Way

Imagine the beauty and luxury of your own natural garden and a fruit orchard inhabited by bees making golden honey right outside your home. You wouldn't have to go far to find abundant streams full of fish and forests stocked with deer and game. Your buffet would be organic, full of natural minerals and free of pollution and additives. What a paradise! Only cold, dry or harsh climatic conditions, or two-legged enemies, would deny the guarantee of daily abundance.

While the Plains Indians had all the buffalo they could eat, agricultural tribes sought their meat sources from the animals living in the woods and around lakes. Animals eaten included rabbit, squirrel, deer, raccoon, opossum, bear, woodchuck, porcupine, beaver, turtles, and wild hog. Birds sought for food were wild turkeys, geese, duck, dove and quail. All varieties of fish, including crawfish and the amphibian frog and turtle, were caught and roasted.

Natural foods are the best to cure or prevent disease by nourishing healthy cellular structures with nutrients such as minerals, vitamins and enzymes. These, in turn, feed glands, endocrine systems and nervous systems, which enrich blood and help vital organs.

Today, we don't want to go out to kill raccoon for food or have to scour for wild vegetables. It takes knowledge to obtain proper nutrients, but it can be done. American grocery stores are a marvel of plenty; the supply and variety of food available is unequaled in history. Unfortunately, temptation to eat nonnutritious foods is strong. The more altered the natural foodstuff, the less likely original nutrients are present. One result is that there is little cancer in agricultural societies compared to industrial ones.

There is evidence of arthritis and rheumatism in Indians, afflictions which are thought to have resulted from sleeping outside and performing hard labor in all kinds of weather (like lugging a buffalo through the snow)! Famine, droughts and living in harsh climates with dangerous conditions contributed to evidence of prehistoric disease. The Indians had no modern dentists and evidence of tooth decay exists. However, dental problems increased in proportion to the quantities of the white man's diet consumed.

Fatality rates for Native Americans increased drastically during forced marches to reservations and imprisonment. After all the buffalo were killed by white men, and the government fed Indians rations, they were forced to eat white flour instead of whole-grain corn flour or wild rice and sugar in place of fruit and honey. Today, Native Americans, just like average Americans, eat a diet not unlike the one they had to learn to eat on reservations as well as fast food and nonnutritious drinks. Today, Native Americans on reservations have a fifty percent chance of dying of diabetes-related organ failure. Their diet bears little resemblance to that of their ancestors. Their physical constitutions are ill-suited to the white flour, white sugar, processed-food diet of modern America. Indian fry bread, made of white flour and prized today by everyone except health-food advocates, was born from army rations and hunger.

There still exist areas in the world where people eat natural foods and report longevity and freedom from disease. Hunza Valley residents in Nepal report villagers of 120 years old and up. One resident, thought to be the oldest living person, was a 140-year-old woman. In 1987, she was televised dancing and smoking a cigarette but unfortunately, she died shortly afterward, perhaps from the excitement or perhaps from old age.

These villagers live at a high altitude, eat natural foods, eat some meat, especially in the winter, walk on mountainous terrain and, interestingly, make decisions communally. The individual, then, is shielded from surviving alone. Until recently, outsiders could not enter the valley and even today permission is required to travel into this isolated, mountainous area where the altitude rises to 20,000 feet. The geographic makeup provides protection and reduces environmental stress by thwarting invasion.

As already discussed, the Native American shamans knew that various factors contributed to the effects of herbs or medicine on the body. The milieu is all-important.

Healing, then, is a complex process. While we can't control our culture, heredity and environment, we do have control over our own health in terms of food selection. The author finds it peculiar that large groups of people haven't any concerns about how they treat their physical bodies (or mental bodies) even though they have to live in them for their lifetimes and suffer the consequences of neglect. Your health begins to improve automatically with a reverence for your physical self (desire to care for yourself) and the consequent actions taken.

The change in diet requires no expensive foods and can be accomplished by eating simply. The southwestern Native American diet of yesteryear, still the diet of traditional Mexican and

Native American families, ranks supreme. It has the same balance of food nutrients recommended and recently "discovered" by modern dietitians. Corn, bean and rice combinations contain complete proteins and the complex carbohydrates which are so important for good health. Corn is high in essential amino acids (needed for protein) except lysine and isoleucine. These are supplied by the amino acids in pinto beans, which in turn lack tryptophan and sulphur acids, which are supplied by corn.

Adding vegetables like squashes, peppers, onions, tomatoes, avocados, potatoes and greens makes a tasty and nutritious blend. Fruit and nuts round off the diet. Capsicum (hot red pepper) is an invaluable herb in the native diet that provides increased blood circulation and lymph-gland cleansing. It contains high doses of vitamin A and is a cardiovascular healing agent for the heart.

Meat, a body tonic, is needed for strength and protein, especially for growing children and menstruating and lactating women, who need natural iron from red meat and high protein diets. Sedentary adults do not need meat three times a day. It is a chief contributor to colon cancer and glandular weakness. Today, children and adults need deep-sea food for protein and mineral content. People who are particularly interested in longevity include sardines and salmon in their diets.

Mexican cheese is a healthy, low-fat cheese that is soft and easily melted. Until recently, it was available only in Mexican markets or southwestern grocery stores, but it is gaining popularity. Like tortillas, it supplies calcium.

Pipitas (pumpkin seeds) are a delicious snack for adults and children and a valuable antiparasitic treatment. Increase their strength by combining herbal pumpkin capsules or raw pumpkin seeds with garlic, sage and black walnut tincture. Pumpkin seeds are invaluable in maintaining the health of the prostate gland and female organs. Middle-aged men, along with the rest of the population, should use pipitas as a routine snack. Purchase raw pumpkin seeds at your health-food store.

New flavored deserts like sopaipillas (white flour) are a favorite dessert, served with honey. Choose local raw honey for the best health benefits. If you were to eat the southwestern diet, you could then afford to eat a dessert of Indian fry bread or a sopaipilla.

Wild rice, a grain instead of a true rice, is native around lakes in northern states. It is a tall grass that grows in water and is harvested by hand from canoes even today, and thus is expensive. The Menominee Indians in Wisconsin and Michigan regarded it as their main food source (it supplied twenty-five percent of their diet) and honored this plant instead of corn. It has the highest grain protein of all the cereals, furnishing close to twenty percent protein by weight. Fish and game supplied the remainder of the high-protein diet available to the Native Americans living in the Great Lakes region.

Today, gourmet cooks serve wild rice as an accompaniment to meat for visiting diplomats unfamiliar with the grain or serve it as a dressing with quail or duck. At home, mix it with regular rice or serve with vegetables. It is a versatile, tasty food and is also good mixed with cranberries or other fruit.

Jerusalem artichokes, also called sunchokes, a member of the sunflower family, had their name taken from the Italian word *girasole,* which means "turning to the sun." Mispronounced by other Europeans as Jerusalem, the name remains. The artichoke is native to the Americas and was taken to Europe by the French. Different tribes ate the root raw, baked or boiled. The tuber looks like a cross between a potato and a gingerroot. The fresh root is prized by diabetics because it contains inulin (not insulin), that keeps its sugar from being absorbed by the body and only has about seven calories. During storage it builds up sugar that can be absorbed, reaching a maximum calorie count of about eighty per tuber. Today, Jerusalem artichokes are served stir-fried, boiled or creamed like a potato. They are a good substitute for water chestnuts in recipes.

Unfortunately, Americans' digestive systems are sensitive to highly nutritious foodstuffs due to a dirth of proper fiber, starvation of essential nutrients, and lack of exercise. These factors, combined with overeating, have caused people to avoid these nutritional foods because they cause "digestive distubances"! Slowly begin to build up your body and rebuild cellular structures. Cellular growth is a constant, ongoing process.

# Eating Natural Native Foods Today

## Corn

Indians used every part of the corn plant. Besides being the number one foodstuff, corn products provided diverse services. Warmed cornmeal with comfrey leaves provided a poultice for sores and swelling. Corn silk added to hot water made a tea or flavored stews. Corn silk boiled in water added flavor and nutrition. Native Americans used the ground meal to clean leather garments, and cooked food in the leaves (like our tamales today). Corn oil provided relief for dry skin and scalp. Corn was made into hominy with wood ashes, succotash by adding beans, and pemmican by drying with fruit.

The Spanish word for cooked cornmeal is *polenta.* It is eaten by people the world over, from tiny, low-income homes to five-star gourmet restaurants serving *haute cuisine.* It is easily prepared, inexpensive and highly versatile when combined with condiments suitable for different cultures and taste-buds. Settlers observed Indians cooking it as a cereal, and named it bear mush. Originally from the New World it rapidly spread to Europe during the seventeenth century.

# Cooking Cornmeal

For the purest and most nutritious polenta, choose organic whole-grain yellow cornmeal. Ordinary cornmeal found in grocery stores is degermed for a longer shelf life. Degermed cereals like wheat or corn don't spoil and are not as likely to attract weevils, as they don't contain the highly nutritious "germ," or seed of the plant. Health-food stores typically carry a number of whole-grain corn meal grinds and mixes, as do upscale food markets .

## POLENTA-CORNMEAL MUSH

INGREDIENTS:
*1 cup whole cornmeal*
*4 cups water*

Stir cornmeal into cold water before heating on the stove. This is the secret to preventing lumps. Bring to a boil, stirring frequently. Follow the directions on the package for length of time. Unprocessed cornmeal will take about twenty to twenty-five minutes or until the raw taste is gone. Preprocessed grits or quick polenta cereals may cook in five minutes. The latter are handier but cost more and, due to processing, may provide fewer nutrients. The longer cooking and coarser grains require attention and time (for stirring). Polenta can be cooked beforehand and reheated.

When it cools, cooked corn mush has the interesting characteristic of hardening into any shape in which it was poured. It can be sliced when cold and, when reheated, will retain that form. Or it can be reheated and stirred back into a hot cereal. In Italy, it is cut into pieces and served with sauce, like a pasta. Gourmet restaurants use it for every type of dish, including desserts. Pour leftover cooked (and still hot) corn mush into a pan, glass dish or cookie sheet that has the shape you want. Or leave it in the pan in which it was cooked and refrigerate until you want to reheat it.

## INSTANT BREAKFAST CORNMEAL PANCAKES

After previously cooking polenta, and while it is hot, pour it onto a cookie sheet. Chill until the next morning. Using a can of the size you want the pancakes, cut the cold polenta into rounds as though you are using a cookie cutter. Heat the rounds in a little cooking oil and serve with applesauce, maple syrup, raw honey or fruit.

To serve polenta as a main dish, slice pieces into pastalike strips and serve them in place of spaghetti in Italian dishes, or use the round pieces like tortillas and serve them in a favorite Mexican dish.

## BRUNCH OR LUNCH POLENTA

Cook the cornmeal as above for mush. Pour the hot meal on a plate and add soft-cooked eggs and/or beans. Serve with green chili sauce, enchilada sauce or tomato salsa. You can add sautéed chopped onions to any of the sauces. Leftover heated polenta can be used to save time.

## DINNER POLENTA

Sauté onions and garlic in olive oil and then add spaghetti or marinara sauce, with or without meat. Serve on a platter over cooked polenta. Garnish with grated Parmesan cheese. Or just serve polenta with a generous amount of unsalted butter and freshly grated Parmesan cheese.

## Grits

Grits is a coarse cornmeal traditionally served as breakfast fare in the southern part of the United States. It is usually served with butter as a side dish. Gourmet yellow corn grits are available and contain vitamin A. White corn grits are the most common.

## Corn-on-the-Cob

One of the best and most fun summer dishes is a huge platter of steaming-hot corn-on-the-cob. At peak season, try to buy corn at a vegetable stand. Purchase as many ears fresh or frozen as your family wants to eat. Boil the ears in a large pot until tender, test at three minutes for young corn, four or five minutes for mature. Serve with butter, salt, and pepper. Use corn holders as handles if you have them. Chew kernels well.

## Corn Bread

Experiment with whole-grain corn meal mixes or make your own. Recipe: Grease and flour a 8-inch-square pan and preheat oven to 350 degrees.

MIX TOGETHER:
*1 cup stone-ground yellow cornmeal*
*1 cup whole-wheat pastry flour*
*¼ tsp. salt*
*2 tsp. baking soda*

MIX TOGETHER:
*2 eggs*
*3 tbsp. honey*
*⅓ cup corn or other vegetable oil*
*1¼ cup buttermilk*

Blend the above dry and wet ingredients, using as few strokes as possible. Immediately place in hot oven to bake for twenty or twenty-five minutes or until knife blade comes out clean. Butter and serve with beans and greens. Freeze leftover bread and reheat later in microwave on defrost setting, wrapping bread in a paper towel. For those not wanting to "nuke" their homemade nutritious bread, wrap in foil and heat in oven on "warm."

## INDIAN FRY BREAD

Make your Indian fry bread more nutritious by making it with all or part whole wheat pastry flour with a little wheat germ added.

INGREDIENTS:

*2 eggs*
*1 cup milk*
*2 cups whole-wheat pastry flour*
*1¾ cup white flour*
*¼ cup wheat germ*
*½ tsp. salt*
*2 tsp. baking powder*

Beat eggs, add milk. Stir in the rest of the ingredients and roll out pastry on plastic or floured board until thin. Cut into squares or triangles. Fry in deep fat until lightly browned. Poke a hole in the middle if you don't want the pieces to puff up. Or let them puff out and serve with honey as a type of sopaipilla. Serve fry bread flat or filled with pinto beans, lettuce, tomatoes and cheese, with salsa and green chili on the side.

## Beans

The fastest way to cook dry pinto beans is in a pressure cooker. If you have several hours, cover the beans with water and bring to a boil in a pot. Boil for about ten minutes and remove from the heat and let stand covered until the pot stops boiling. Bring the pot back to a boil and then reduce the heat to simmer the beans until done, about two hours. Add water as needed. Cook with onion for extra flavor and season to taste after done. Southern and midwestern cooks season with ham, preferably on the bone.

Bean pots are handy for those who want to leave them on all day while you are away. Serve the beans with corn bread and greens for a balanced protein meal. Mash leftover beans with a potato masher and make them into a bean dip.

## BEAN SALAD

Enjoy the two native bean varieties, kidney and black-eyed peas, in a cold salad.

Combine: cooked and cooled or canned black-eyed peas, kidney beans, and green beans together with sweet green pepper or canned pimiento. Toss with a mixture of two tablespoons salad oil, two tablespoons apple cider vinegar, a little garlic powder, one teaspoon sugar, and slices from a large red onion.

## TEN-MINUTE HOMEMADE ENCHILADAS

In large skillet, layer enchilada sauce and purchased corn tortillas. Top with thin sliced onion and processed low-fat cheese or Mexican cheese. Heat until hot all the way through and cheese is melted. Use three tortillas, one small can enchilada sauce, two tablespoons onion and one ounce cheese for each serving. Serve with beans and guacamole salad.

## Guacamole Salad

Chop up and blend together three avocados, one large tomato, one tablespoon lime or lemon juice, two tablespoon fresh cilantro leaves, and salt to taste. Add a tiny bit of finely diced jalapeno pepper, taste and add more if desired for a hotter salad. Serve with corn chips.

## Posole

*Quick Method:* Use canned hominy. In a skillet, brown ground beef, onions, red chili pepper and a little garlic salt. Add hominy and heat.

*Longer Method:* Soak dried hominy overnight in water or use pressure cooker. If desired, use the bean-cooking method described above. Add same ingredients as for quick method. Tex-Mex recipes add a little tomato sauce.

The northern recipes are different in that they use pork chunks (cut cooked pork into one-inch cubes) added to the hominy with green chili sauce (it's hot) and cilantro or oregano.

## Popcorn

Have a fun Sunday night supper at home with an all-you-can-eat popcorn night. Kids enjoy it and it will provide needed fiber they probably aren't getting. Popcorn can also be served in a bowl with milk for extra protein. For your adult friends, pop one-half cup dried popcorn in corn oil in which you have added one teaspoon of liquid capsicum pepper. Sprinkle with a mixture of regular chili powder (two teaspoons) and black pepper, or pour several tablespoons of melted butter over popcorn and sprinkle with several tablespoons of chopped cilantro and serve.

## The Pumpkin Squash Family

The pumpkin and its cousin, the squash, are valuable vegetables too often overlooked, except perhaps on holidays.

The prolific master squash is zucchini because of its versatility, size, and the number of squash produced by a single plant you could easily grow in your backyard. The word *squash* comes from an Indian word meaning eaten raw, as that was the way Native Americans ate the vegetable.

Soft summer squash was eaten off the vine or cooked with stew. Pumpkin was dried raw and braided and eaten when hunger struck.

### SOFT SQUASH

Cut summer squash (yellow crookneck, zucchini, yellow straight-neck, scalloped squash) into slices. Sauté in a little oil with a little water added and cover until tender.

For a heartier meal, mix sliced squash and a generous supply of sliced onions together in a skillet. Add canned tomatoes and cook until tender.

### WINTER SQUASH

The winter squashes are actually the product sold as canned pumpkin because of their superior flavor. They are best eaten as is, baked in the oven with a little butter, and served with maple sugar or honey. Just cut in half, lay the cut side down in a little water, and bake for about forty-five minutes at 350 degrees. The spaghetti squash looks like a winter squash but is low in calories and fun to eat. When you scoop out the pulp after it is cooked, it resembles spaghetti and is served with pasta sauce or butter.

## Indian Summer Salad

Add to your food processor (shredding disc) about two-thirds cup each of the following cleaned and peeled raw vegetables: sugar or miniature pumpkin, zucchini, parsnips, red cabbage, sunchokes (Jerusalem artichokes), and carrots. Add three-quarters cup pinon nuts, walnuts or pecans if desired. Add about one-half cup vinegar and oil dressing. Chill.


## Baked Pumpkins

Pumpkins are great fun and good to eat if you buy the small miniature ones or the three-pound variety known as sugar pumpkins. The larger varieties make fun decorations for children and interesting serving dishes for meals but are not as flavorful when cooked.

Cut the lid off a sugar pumpkin, leaving about a 2-inch stem. Scoop out seeds, rinse out leaving a little water inside, and bake on a pie plate. For a three-pound sugar pumpkin, bake for about an hour at 325 degrees. If you are cooking miniatures, repeat preparation procedure but cook for only about twenty minutes, or until done. Children love these pumpkins filled with other vegetables, with pumpkin custard for dessert or seasoned with butter and honey.


## Unbaked Pumpkin

For a great holiday or fun meal, cut the top off a "jack-o-lantern" pumpkin, keeping the top and its stem to use as a lid. Let the kids decorate the pumpkin but don't put any holes in it. Remove the seeds and pulp and warm the pumpkin in an oven. Fill it with your favorite stew or thick soup. To make pumpkin soup, mix one can of prepared cooked pumpkin, one-half cup of whipping cream or evaporated milk, one small can of chicken consommé, and salt and pepper to taste. Serve the soup from the pumpkin.

## Pumpkin Pie Cake

Grease and flour a 9-by-13-inch pan and preheat the oven to 350 degrees.

Spoon canned, prepared pumpkin pie filling (not canned pumpkin without flavoring) into the prepared pan. Sprinkle with one box yellow or white cake mix. Drizzle with one-half cup melted margarine and spinkle one cup of pecans on top. Do not stir. Bake fifty minutes or until tester comes out clean.

## Watermelon

Experts' opinions about the origin of the watermelon vary. Reports from early explorers stated that they saw it growing, yet it is believed by others to be an import from Africa. Whatever the source, it is a valuable food and tonic for the kidneys and bladder, for reducing diets and for doing modified fasts. Give your body a rest from food for a day by eating only watermelon. Because it contains fiber, is easily digested, and ninety percent water, it will help cleanse sluggish kidneys and digestive systems. Eat as much of the melon as you want anyway you like during the day. Diabetics need medical advice for any type of fasting.

Watermelon seeds are an herbal remedy for the kidneys. Crush leftover dried seeds in a coffee grinder and brew in a tea. Or purchase your watermelon seeds from an herbal tea company.

## Pepitas

While raw pumpkin seeds are the best herbal remedy, pumpkin seeds that you scoop out of your sugar pumpkin are good roasted. Separate them from the pulp, and toss them with one tablespoon of light vegetable oil and one-half teaspoon salt for every cup of seeds. Spread the seeds out on a cookie sheet and bake in a 250 degree oven until they are dried out, about forty-five minutes.

For a nutritious supplement, buy raw seeds and eat them as a snack or grind them in your coffee grinder to add to cold or hot cereal. Add ground seeds or wheat germ to children's cereal and they won't be the wiser but will be getting healthier.

## Sunflower Seeds

If you live in a sunny climate, grow sunflowers in your yard for fun and then harvest the seeds to eat or leave them for the birds. If you choose the latter, buy yourself and your family sunflower seeds at the store to use as a nutritious snack.

## Cayenne
### (Capsicum frutescens)

Cayenne pepper is the hot red chili pepper used in Indian, Mexican, and "Tex-Mex" cooking. It is recognized as a valuable herbal remedy and food. It is a general stimulant and serves to aid digestion, increase circulation of the blood, help the heart's action, and keep lymph glands functional. It contains large amounts of vitamin A and minerals. Take it when you feel a cold coming on. Used externally, it stops bleeding. Used internally, a large dose of liquid cayenne might restore heartbeat after congestive heart failure. When eaten daily, it helps prevent sickness. Capsules can be purchased for those who don't like the hot taste.

## Corn Silk

(STIGMATA MAYDIS)

Corn silk, from the corn plant, is one of the best herbal remedies for urinary tract irritations. It is a diuretic (helps expel urine from the body) and consequently lowers blood pressure. Women benefit from taking herbal capsules before menstrual periods to help reduce swelling. It is also useful as a demulcent (contains a soothing and slippery nature) and is helpful with constipation. As with other herbal remedies, it can be purchased in capsule, tincture, or natural form (corn silk from the plant).

*Dose:* Take several herbal capsules whenever a diuretic is desired or to help soothe an irritated bladder or bowel. It is a mild herb and can be drunk in quantity as a tea.

## CORNSTARCH

One of the safest and most soothing, protective, absorbent baby powders, cornstarch is better for babies than commercial baby powder, which is talcum with additives. It is safer for men and women to use than dusting powder in high-risk cancer areas like the chest, underarms and groin.

# 6 Cleansing Herbs

The savage medicine men, declared Father Pierre Biard in 1611, were 'sorcerers, Jugglers, liars, and cheats.' Moreover,' all their science consists in a knowledge of a few simple laxatives, or astringents, hot or cold applications, lenitives or irritants for the liver or kidneys, leaving the rest to luck nothing more. But they are well versed in tricks and impositions.'[37]

American colonists didn't know why American Indians fasted, used sweat baths, purged, believed in cleansing the colon, and, amazingly, believed in washing. The East Coast Indians that greeted the arriving colonists bathed daily, scrubbing with soft plants, while the colonists believed that sitting in water made you sick. Soap and germs were undiscovered.

Native Americans lived in a bountiful environment, had an established social system, bathed in clear streams or hot springs, were unified in their clan religion, and still believed they needed to undergo processes which purified the body from the inside out.

Early pioneers, escaping from religious persecution, starvation or criminal prosecution flocked, or were shipped, to the New World. They were hardly in a position to judge the "savage," a term used by early Europeans to describe the Native Americans.

In his book, *American Indian Medicine*, Virgil Vogel points out that there is no question that the American Indians independently discovered the enema tube and bulb syringe and that their use was widespread. Animal or fish bladders were used in conjunction with inserts made from small hollow bones or reeds. Vogel quotes early reports of Indian medical practice:

> Pierre Charlevoix was certain that the Indians were 'in possession of secrets and remedies which are admirable'.... 'A broken bone was immediately set and was perfectly solid in eight days time'. Of especial importance is his observation in 1721 of the use of enema syringes: 'In the northern parts they made much use of glisters, a bladder was their instrument for this purpose. They have a remedy for the bloody-flux which seldom or never fails; this is a juice expressed from the extremities of cedar branches after they have been well boiled.'

Native Americans believed that purging the body was a necessary precursor to religious rites (for the shaman) and healing rites (for the patient), regardless of the suspected reason for the illness. Sweat lodges, fasting, syringes and strong herbal mixtures promoted excretion of unwanted substances through perspiration (diaphoretic), vomiting (emetic) or ejection through the bowels (cathartic).

These cleansing practices, except for vomiting, continue to grow in popularity with certain health-oriented advocates. Enthusiasts attest to the benefits. If Native Americans used innerbody cleansing techniques, how badly do you think overfed, underexercised, overmedicated and chemically overloaded

Americans need such methods! Yet they are generally avoided or considered unmentionable by the medical profession, including gastroenterologists, and the general public.

Dr. Bernard Jensen, an authority on colonics, recently gave a lecture in the writer's hometown; at the time he was approaching the age of ninety! Mr. V. E. Irons, a pioneer colon-cleansing advocate and researcher, married a woman fifty years younger and fathered children in his eighties. Another enthusiast, Dr. Norman Walker, varyingly reported to be 106 to 116 years-old drowned while swimming in the ocean.

As noted in the chronicles of early settlers, the idea of cleansing the body inside and out was widely practiced and accepted by Native Americans. Soap didn't achieve widespread use in Europe until the mid-1800s when Pasteur discovered germs. Colonists noted that Native Americans in the southwest and as far north as the Dakotas used natural substances such as yucca root (called soap root) to wash themselves, their hair, and their clothes.

Original sweating procedures primarily focused on healing a sick patient, or preparing the medicine man or woman for ceremony or vision. Sweating was usually followed by jumping into a river, and sage leaves were then used to dry and purify the person. Fasting and colon cleansing routinely accompanied the sweat. Beverages with powerful ingredients promoted vomiting and visions preparing medicine leaders for strenuous rites and journeys.

Navajo healing rituals often took seven days, during which time the sick child or adult didn't eat! It was believed fasting helped heal the problem; cooks in Navajo schools knew when a child was fasting and didn't serve him. Navajo medicine leaders today claim to cure people of cancer when traditional doctors have given up hope.

One of the last older Dakota medicine men, Elmer Running,

requires four-day fasts without food or water for his vision quests if the person is healthy. The true medicine healer will "know" the condition of the person he is treating and prescribe accordingly. While Indians believe ritualistic healing procedures lose power if tradition is not followed, old methods, which blended over time with Christian elements, vary widely with each medicine man and woman, even within tribes. Remember, missionaries have been "saving" Indians for five hundred years, with the result that all have a mixture of belief systems. For this reason it is up to the person to choose a "shaman" carefully and not do anything that doesn't feel right. Pseudo–medicine men and women may have little information about safety procedures. Unfortunately, young Indian shamans don't always know the old ways because their religion, being shamed, wasn't learned. On the other hand, there are young Native Americans possessing divine talents and healing information received from above.

## Sweating as Cleansing

Methods for encouraging perspiration varied with climate and terrain. Native Americans enjoyed bathing in hot springs if they were available. After a hot bath, one could bury oneself in mud for a healthy body skin mask or cool off in cold water.

Medicine men or groups of councils or societies used caves or sweat huts. River rocks heated in a center fireplace and dowsed with water send huge clouds of steam on occupants. Rising temperatures brought on loss of body fluid through the skin. Sitting in a confined steam bath, whether in a lodge or hot spring, promoted sweating, a necessary procedure to help the body dispose of unwanted toxins.

Traditional sweat-dwelling openings faced the east as this is the direction of the rising sun. Today, the sweat lodge has expanded from the traditional use by Native Americans to being a popular therapy for anyone interested in serious cleansing of a physical or spiritual nature.

In certain states, like Arizona, there is resentment toward white men who lead traditional sweat ceremonies, sometimes with good reason. While skilled native leaders have intuitive and spiritual communicative skills to receive help from nature beings, these qualities may be absent in inexperienced or nonspiritual sweat lodge leaders. After hundreds of years of religious ridicule, Native Americans resent Caucasians "playing Indian."

The author saw an eagle drop a feather on one vision quest/sweat lodge led by an experienced, full-blooded Lakota, Gary Bear Heals. An *umbleche* (vision quest) led by him brought on an unusual cloud formation that totally surrounded the camp. When you looked up, it was like a view from the bottom of a giant fishbowl.

On numerous occasions, the author has seen tiny lights flickering all around ceremonial teepees with experienced leaders of Indian and non-Indian descent. With inexperienced leaders, there is more likelihood of the sweat being dangerous (for example, using the wrong river rocks could result in an explosion that injures the participants). Misuse of ceremonial procedures is considered sacrilege.

Generally speaking, with several notable exceptions, sweat lodges done by competent leaders of any racial heritage have contributed benefits to participants throughout the United States and Europe. The benefits of hot springs have long been known to Americans, as the number of visitors to these springs attests. In addition to the sweating process, hot mineral springs feed the body extra nutrients that are absorbed through the skin.

Participants need to monitor their own heartbeats as temperatures rise, whether in their own Jacuzzis or in formal sweat lodges led by an "expert." Some leaders think the hotter the better for spiritual growth!

The writer recommends wearing a illuminated watch with a second hand and monitoring your heartbeat during your first sweat. Tell your leader you want to sit by the door and may have to leave if you heart rate gets too high. This is especially important for people with heart trouble in the family.

As in aerobics, never exceed eighty percent of your maximum heart rate and always start with sixty percent of the maximum heart rate in a sweat. To compute your maximum heart rate, subtract your age from 220. Thus, if you are forty-eight years old, your maximum heart rate would be 172 beats per minute. If there is a question of safety at your maximum heart rate, don't go over sixty percent at the outset. For example, 103 beats per minute for a forty-eight-year-old (sixty percent of 172) is a conservative figure for the first sweat. For a person used to exercising and using good health habits, do not exceed eighty percent (138 for a forty-eight year-old). This heartbeat rate should not be allowed for more than twenty minutes in the first sweat, thirty minutes in the second. As your body gradually acclimates to the load of chemicals being purged and becomes less toxic, you will want to stay for the whole procedure.

The average person with typical health habits, or one who is overstressed, will be shocked at how fast their heart rate accelerates if the sweat is a hot one. This is why a watch with an illuminated second hand is recommended (it is dark in a sweat lodge). For a quick reading, take a ten-second reading of your pulse by pressing the carotid artery in your neck or the artery in your wrist. Multiply the count by six to get a one minute rate. For example, heart rate of 17 beats in ten seconds is a 103 beats per minute, a sixty percent level for a forty-eight-year-old. If your heart rate exceeds your maximum, leave the sweat.

Fasting and colon cleansing will accelerate health gains, but for the novice should be done several days before or after the sweat, not at the same time. Perspiration sweats out bodily poisons that accrued late in our bodies due to the insecticides and toxins in our environment. Americans are on toxic overload. Prolonged sweats draw out toxins stored in the tissues, thereby reducing the risk of arrythmia brought on by their presence in the bloodstream. Starting slowly and working up to longer sweats is recommended. Begin by doing your sweat baths at home or in a friend's hot tub.

I have never heard of anyone having a heart attack or dying in a sweat lodge, so perhaps the guardian Indian spirits accompany those involved. The alcoholic and drug treatment movements have found sweat lodges and other Native American practices to have widespread effectiveness and healing power. Men's bonding groups are attending these sweats, as well as mixed male/female and female-only groups. Metaphysical stores and groups usually have notices or information for those wanting to try the experience. In addition to the cleansing aspects, the spiritual group experience is inspiring and brings unexpected rewards.

## Doing a Sweat Cleansing at Home

If you want to do a sweat at home, or to supplement your group sweat experience, you will achieve a positive health result. You will need the following diaphoretic herbs:

1. Elderberry leaves or berries to brew for a tea
2. Peppermint leaves, or cayenne pepper to flavor tea and increase perspiration
3. Crystallized ginger, in candy form, to help you enjoy yourself and also increase perspiration

Prepare your bed to protect your mattress from your own sweat. Take off customary bedding. Place a plastic sheet protector, shower curtain, or tablecloth across the mattress. Cover with a washable mattress cover. Have several washable heavy blankets ready on the bed to use as covers. Place several sheets or large towels by your bath to use when you get up.

Prepare your elderberry tea by pouring boiling water over the herb and letting it steep while you prepare your bath. Sit a potful next to your tub. Take as hot a bath as you can stand, or use your Jacuzzi. As your bath water cools, keep running more hot water into the tub. Drink as much of the tea as you can while you eat some ginger. Just as you do in any sweating procedure, time yourself or monitor your heartbeat.

When you get out, wrap up, take your teapot and ginger, go to your protected bed, and wrap up in your blankets. You will continue to sweat just like you were in the tub. Stay there until you cool off, from thirty minutes to an hour. Stay quiet, sip more tea and congratulate yourself on beginning your detoxification program. Afterward take a shower and use a skin brush or sponge to scrub. Don't plan any activities except quiet ones until bedtime.

## MUD BATH

Used in expensive salons and health farms, the mud bath can be done at home. If you live on a farm you can find a muddy spot and on a warm day cover yourself with the mud and lie out to dry. If you are an urban resident, you will need to purchase bentonite—natural clay. It is sold in bags in beauty-supply or health-food stores.

Choosing a warm day, or a warm patio, mix the betonite with water, and cover yourself with a thick layer on one side or one part of your body, unless you have enough to lie down in, in which case then cover up with it. Let the mud dry and then rinse it off outside. For small applications, buy the brand-name jars of bentonite and use it at night for a facial or for selected blemishes. Queen Helene and Aztec Secret Health and Beauty both sell jars of inexpensive clay packs.

The psychic healer Edgar Cayce advocated castor-oil packs for certain parts of the body to aid arthritis and the organs. Just heat castor oil, pour on a soft towel and apply to area such as the gall bladder, liver or colon. Using a heating pad over the towel will keep it warm.

## Colon Cleansing Today

Indians used devices to perform enemas to rid the body of trapped or undesirable contents of the intestines and for spiritual reasons (to make themselves purer in order to communicate with sacred guides).

Wealthy Americans used health spas such as those owned by the Kellogg cereal family, one of the first institutions to recommend colon cleansing and fiber consumption (the Kellogg brothers invented packaged cereal). Public figures such as Mae West and John Lennon were among those who valued colonics to keep them looking good and feeling healthy. Over the years and even today, movie stars routinely have used some form of colon cleansing to keep their figures and skin toned.

In 1979, *Cosmopolitan* magazine published an article on "High Colonic Irrigation" by Carol Signorella, a New York City reporter:

> After a year of colonics, my appearance and energy levels were both radically improved. No more draggy mornings or late-afternoon slumps. The bags under my eyes had disappeared entirely, and the sallow, yellowish tone that had spoiled my skin has been replaced by a healthy glow. I seem to think more clearly now, and I need less sleep. In a word, both my body and mind feel marvelously *clean*.

The average allopathic modern doctor believes there is no toxic carryover from an impacted colon to other parts of the body. Medical tests that are available to measure blood contamination from the colon, as well as tests to find parasite contamination, are rarely used. One only has to walk through the drugstore and wonder at the shelves of laxatives to know that a problem exists. There are books that document the side effects of parasite infestation (common in congested intestines), but neither congestion nor its side effects are dealt with during physicals or medical visits.

One sign of progress has been the increasing knowledge of the value of increased fiber in the diet (health advocates have known about it for decades)! When you begin to cleanse the intestines, you instantly feel better and the surrounding tissues get healthier. Fiber in the diet, exercise, and the desire to improve your health all begin to help cleanse the inner you. Unfortunately, spastic or damaged colons may not benefit from added fiber, as it builds up in the colon. Today various syringes and devices for colon cleansing are used: enema bags, professional colonic equipment in clinics, or coloma boards that you can use in your home. In the health-food stores, you will find books to help you learn how to use these devices. Recommended: Dr. Bernard Jensen's Book, *Tissue Cleansing Through Bowel Management*, and Dr. Norman Walker's book, *Colonic Therapy*. Dr. Jensen gives you specific directions for using a coloma board at home.

The importance of proper sanitary maintenance of this equipment, especially in clinics, can't be overstated. Once you are assured of this, health and chiropractic clinics have colonic therapists to help you. Less costly are home supplies that require some practice and education to use properly. It is usually worth the time and effort to learn the proper procedures to use at home so that you can maintain privacy and assure proper hygiene—unless you have more money than time. Good health-food stores carry the necessary supplies.

Herbal laxatives were used by Native Americans as both preventative and purgative measures. Herbal laxatives don't remove old, impacted colon contents, but are useful for temporary constipation and purging. Colon cleansing attempts to remove impacted fecal matter and takes time and patience. It is not a quick fix, although you will think so after your first three-day fast (seeing what comes out).

Diabetics, cancer and degenerative-disease patients, or people with abdominal pain or suspected appendicitis shouldn't undertake colon-cleansing fasts unless they are under the strict supervision of an expert. Unfortunately, people with advanced diverticulitis (pockets in the colon) may not be able to tolerate the water cleansing internally, as their colons may be abscessed. However, early stages of diverticulitis can be cured, so this is a difficult call. Please consult your medical doctor if you have any of these problems. X-ray examination will show the extent of the colon pocketing if you want to make the decision yourself. As a general rule, the longer the existence of diverticulitis and the older the person, the more reason to avoid using enema procedures.

Dr. Bernard Jensen recommends drinking watered-down apple juice with fiber and supplements to help move out hardened material stored in the bowels. The one- or three-day juice cleanse is a modified type of fast. Directions about time sequences and any supplements needed should be followed. Fasting while taking psyllium fiber followed by pancreatin enzymes begins immediately to move material out of the cells of the body including the intestines.

Start with the one-day or three-day apple juice cleansing program described below. A month later try a three-day juice cleansing. Six months later repeat the three-day procedure. This program is a modified version of Dr. Jensen's and is conservative. Once or twice a year repeat the three-day cleansing juice fast.

Repeat the colonics or herbal laxatives as needed. After the colon is strong and healthy enough to function on its own, you will know when it needs an extra cleansing.

A strict water fast is usually too hard on American bodies because toxins present in the fat and body tissues dump into the bloodstream during fasting. Water fasting also does not "pull out" undesirable contents of the colon because the necessary supplements to do so aren't present. The same holds true for ordinary juice fasting, which is hard on the body because there is too much sugar present and, like the water fast, the body has to "absorb" the toxic contents of the colon!

## One-day or Three-day Cleanse/Fast

MATERIALS NEEDED:
One large bottle of apple juice
One container of psyllium hulls
One bottle liquid chlorophyll
One bottle hydrated bentonite
One bottle apple cider vinegar
Vitamin C tablets
Calcium/Magnesium supplement
One six pack of 6-oz. cans of tomato juice or V8 juice
One large bottle of pancreatic enzyme, quadruple strength. This enzyme is essential.

Directions for mixing your cleansing apple juice drink follow these suggestions.

For your first fast, plan to stay at home and rest or watch television. People think they will surely starve to death if they miss one meal, when in truth they may not be hungry all day and may have to force themselves to drink all five drinks. After one fast at home, you may work if you wish; if you are planning to do a three-day fast, work the first day, say on a Friday, and do the next two days over the weekend while at home or running errands.

Depending on your usual schedule, plan to drink the cleansing drink five times during the day. Add one six-ounce can of tomato juice in the early afternoon as juice or heated as a soup. Obese people should add another six-ounce can of tomato or mixed vegetable juice in the evening.

Schedule an enema or colonic at the end of each day and an extra one the next morning if you are continuing the juice fast. It is better not to have to prepare food for anyone else during the day, although some people do better not eating if they are supplementing their own need for food fantasies by cooking for others or rearranging their recipes (thinking of food, not eating it).

## CLEANSING JUICE RECIPE

Pour three or four ounces of apple juice into a large glass.

ADD:
*1 tsp. chlorophyll*
*1 heaping tsp. psyllium hulls (stir well)*
*1 tablespoon hydrated bentonite*
*1 tablespoon apple cider vinegar*
*8 to 10 oz. of water to taste*

Drink immediately, as fiber will thicken.

IMPORTANT: DRINK ANOTHER GLASS OF WATER AN HOUR AFTER EACH JUICE DRINK, TOGETHER WITH SIX TABLETS OF PANCREATIC ENZYME.

*Take 500 mg vitamin C (once or twice a day)*
*Take 1,000 mg calcium-magnesium daily supplement*

*Important: Between cleansing juice fasting days, drink the exact same drink, described above, once a day; omit taking the six tablets of pancreatin.* However, get in the habit of using digestive enzymes after each meal if you're over forty. For example, after a large meal try taking one or two pancreatic enzymes and another with HCL (hydrochloric acid) if meat has been eaten. For meals of fruit, cultured dairy products like yogurt or cottage cheese or juice, you don't need digestives.

## HEALING CRISIS

Trying any new healing or health method, when the mind firmly has decided on improvement, will eventually result in a process known as a "healing crisis." As unwanted chemicals and old deposits wash out, a person's body will go through an adjustment to change and have symptoms as the toxins leave the body. You may not notice it, and if you do, it won't last more than seventy-two hours, the natural time a body needs to adjust itself. For example, people on weight-loss diets notice that the scales don't reflect their loss for seventy-two hours (three days).

A healing crisis usually occurs this way: you will feel better immediately after doing a one-day or three-day juice fast. Then, after the body is "ready," because of newly acquired cellular health, clearing of the tissues begins and symptoms such as feeling a little out of sorts start to manifest themselves. Perhaps you feel bloated or restless and think your efforts to improve your health haven't worked. Sometimes you feel a little dizzy or get a headache, develop a cough, or have a discharge. Undesired toxins, chemicals or other material has moved through the bloodstream, been secreted in perspiration or been passed out through elimination from the intestines.

The healing crisis may go unnoticed if you are used to feeling out of sorts through poor health habits. This cycle of feeling good, having a healing crisis, and then feeling good again is a cycle that is repeated over and over until the body has cleansed itself. The body heals from the inside out, so after the colon begins to cleanse, organs in close proximity will do the same. You only have to remember that it is because you are strong enough that you can have a healing crisis in the first place, because only a healthy body can continually cleanse and get healthier. You are adding years to your life span as you work on your health, provided you add the proper nutrients to your diet at the same time you do your cleansing program.

It wasn't because of "superstition" that Native American medicine leaders fasted and cleansed before ceremonies. *Cleansing actually changes the cellular structure of the body!* Spiritualists believe fasting and cleansing lighten the etheric and astral body of a person raising his vibratory level. This phenomenon explains why after fasting people see "visions" or have glimpses of life in the unseen world. This is why Indians purged and cleansed!

Giving your child anti-histamines to stop a runny nose or using antiperspirants under your arms every day actually stop the natural cleansing process of the body. For this reason, during your health-improvement program please avoid taking pills to stop the flow of natural fluids in the body so the body can cleanse the lymph glands and mucous membranes. Wearing tight pants and bras that restrict circulation, and using talcum powder in the groin and underarm area are thought to contribute to the formation of cancer cells in the body. Babies can be powdered with cornstarch when necessary.

Use natural deodorants (available at the health-food stores), not antiperspirants, and don't use anything when you don't have a reason. Save your antiperspirant for getting up in front of a group. Why would you feel a need when relaxed at home? Later you won't need them because your body odor will disappear.

## Foods to Build Colon Health

The body will only rebuild itself when it is strong enough to replace the cellular structure. It can heal and grow stronger only when it has the proper nutrients to do so. Eating complete foods which contain essential enzymes, vitamins, minerals, and amino acids feeds the glandular, metabolic and endocrine systems in your body to keep you and your vital organs healthy. Herbal supplements contribute to healing. Cleansing per se does not do the repairing. It moves out pollution and impurities which block the rebuilding process. So to gain good health, you have to eat nutritious food. To help you in your cleansing and health-building program, eat from the following list foods that are kind to the colon, digestive system and entire body. These foods are in addition to the supplements, herbs and foods already mentioned in this book, which can be selected according to individual needs.

*Soft cooked cereals* are excellent for the colon:
oatmeal
rice (choose parboiled for a complete food)
cooked, whole-grain corn cereal (polenta)
starchy, hot cereals (add wheat germ for nutrition)

*Vegetables and fruits* good for the colon:
fresh carrot or other vegetable juice
squashes
beets (cooked fresh)
potatoes, white and sweet
avocados
okra
cooked carrots, and other yellow vegetables
bananas
papayas

cantaloupes and other melons
apples and applesauce
mangoes
peaches, apricots, and nectarines
dried figs

*Breads* for the colon:
sour-dough, rye or cracked wheat flour
corn tortillas
unleavened bread products
sprouted grain bread
(avoid white bread and yeast breads)

*Foods with natural acidolphilus culture:*
milk with added acidolphilus
cottage cheese
yogurt
buttermilk
goats' milk
cream cheese (reduced fat)
acidolphilus supplements or powder

*Herbs* to help the colon:
Senna (natural laxative)
Slippery elm (demulcent)
Aloe vera (demulcent)
Cascara sagrada (laxative)
Black cohosh (muscle relaxant)
Wild yam (muscle relaxant)

*Herbs* to help get rid of parasites:
Black walnut
Garlic

Sage
Herbal pumpkin or pumpkin seeds
Wormwood
Onion

## Native American Cleansing Herbs

It is no accident that the procedures and herbs used today to cleanse the internal body are native to North America and were used by the Indians centuries ago. There are two main reasons for this. First, because contemporary allopathic doctors don't believe in internal cleansing, pharmaceutical companies don't see any reason to synthesize natural herbal ingredients as marketable prescription drugs. Second, they work. Thus, ancient herbal remedies are legal, inexpensive and plentiful as well as being effective and safe.

Use of herbal remedies requires common sense and moderation as they do contain ingredients which affect the body. For example, the oils and tinctures of wormwood and black walnut are highly potent and concentrated. You should follow the instructions on the label, as mixture strengths vary by manufacturer and be sure to keep them out of the reach of children!

### Aloe Vera
(AGAVE AMERICANA)

Native Americans drank the juice of the plant and used it to heal wounds and abrasions and soothe dry or sunburned skin. Because Americans have abused their digestive tracts and intestines, thousands drink aloe vera juice daily to promote rebuilding of the colon and small intestines, to help heal ulcers and to use as a gentle laxative.

As the juice is popular, many brands are available. Old favorites include George's Aloe Vera juice and Lily of the Desert juice and gel. The writer prefers the gel for internal cleansing. Avoid brands containing large quantities of preservatives.

Pregnant women should consult their naturopathic physician or medical doctor because of the laxative qualities of the drink, especially for women expected to have trouble carrying their babies to full term. Healthy, pregnant women may find the juice helpful for relieving constipation, but should avoid taking it in large quantities during the last trimester.

Cleansing techniques such as colon irrigation, enemas or hot sweat baths shouldn't be used by pregnant women. Pregnancy is one time you don't want to circulate poisons in the body, even to discharge them. Do your cleansing before you get pregnant. Aloe vera shouldn't be used by people with possible appendicitis or cirrhosis of the liver.

Aloe vera has the added advantage of improving health because it provides carbohydrates and is touted to contain all the essential amino acids. It is believed to help organs and tissues recover from radiation and to help cleanse the liver, spleen, kidney and bladder. To prevent or expel pinworms in children, mix aloe vera juice with fruit juice or dilute it with warm water to use as an enema.

## Senna

(CASSIA MARILANDICA)

Native Americans used senna, a cathartic (laxative), to dispel parasites, purge the colon and, perhaps, to help bring on menstruation or childbirth in unusual circumstances. The bruised root, moistened with water, was used as a dressing for sores and, mixed with water, drunk for sore throats and fevers.

Today senna is combined with fruit leaves or soothing herbs to provide the mildest laxative effects in the bowels. One of the popular senna combinations is sold under the name of Swiss Kriss Tabs and is available in health-food stores.

While natural herbal laxatives are a temporary and necessary fix now and then, they do not clear an impacted colon. That is the purpose of the cleansing diet. Herbal laxatives improve health when used only as needed by keeping material from continuing to gather and lodge in the intestines. People with spastic colons may require sporadic use of mild laxatives as a preventative and should seek medical help or use antispasmodic herbs.

## Cascara Sagrada
(RHAMNUS PURSHIANA)

The Indians used cascara sagrada, which is the bark of the California buckthorn tree, as a laxative. Even in the medical industry, this herb has wide recognition as a laxative and is included in a number of preparations sold in drugstores. Constipation is at an all-time high. Accordingly, pharmaceutical companies have synthesized ingredients from this herb. It is not recommended for spastic colons but seems to be preferred by those with the opposite problem—lazy or untoned bowels. Personality and body structure go together. Judge your own temperament and choose your laxative accordingly. Interestingly, cascara is thought to increase the production of bile which would be needed by those not as easily "galled" and perhaps "looser" in gut and temperament than more uptight types!

## Slippery Elm
(ULMUS FULVA MICHX.)

Slippery elm, widely recognized by Native Americans for its soothing, healing effects, was utilized by Indians all across the United States to help heal deep wounds and to cleanse the body.

Slippery elm comes from the inner bark of the red elm tree. It is slippery and the mucilage is healing and anti-inflammatory. Slippery elm also contains tannins that give it an astringent quality. This combination is good for healing and soothing mucous membranes and the digestive tract.

Today herbologists use slippery elm as an herbal remedy for a variety of digestive disorders such as duodenal ulcers, colitis, gastritis, diarrhea and constipation. In diarrhea, it heals irritated membranes and acts as an inner astringent. In severe cases of diarrhea it should be discontinued, as the slippery qualities, useful in constipation, might contribute to dehydration.

## Castor Oil

Oil from the castor bean is a traditional laxative. It is cultivated extensively in the United States because so many people use it. Do not get in the habit of using this oil as a daily laxative because it depletes the body of vitamins A and E and results in vitamin deficiencies. You can tell those who use it every day: their skin looks like old leather. Castor oil is useful as a laxative after a heavy purging or fasting and for heated oil packs used on the body, as described earlier.

## Black Walnut

(JUGLANS NIGRA)

Black walnut, a vermifuge, is one of the herbal foods used by Native Americans to dispel worms in the body.

Black walnut capsules or tincture can be taken during or after a cleaning fast or any time in between. The tincture is liquid and easily absorbed by the body. Take the recommended dosage for tincture, capsules or other remedy as strength varies. Herbal black walnut is a vermifuge because it contains iodine, a strong disinfectant and toxin to putrefaction. For that reason, it should be kept out of the reach of children.

Black walnut has the added advantage of giving the body needed iodine, essential for thyroid functioning. Midwesterners and other groups of people who don't have access to seafood sometimes develop goiters around the Adam's apple, one result of an iodine deficiency. Everyone's thyroid functioning varies; for those who demonstrate hyperthyroidism (a hyperactive thyroid), taking iodine on a daily basis could cause nervousness, sleeplessness, hair loss and an over-worked heart. This is an individual matter and one which needs assessment from a naturopathic doctor, a person who does muscle testing (kinesiology), or a medical doctor, who can administer thyroid tests.

Eating onions and garlic provides a natural antibiotic for the body and discourages bacteria and parasites. Sage and wormwood are useful herbal treatments for vermine.

One Native American and naturopathic cure for parasites is to eat one cup of raw pumpkin seeds a day for three days while otherwise eating as little as possible. People with delicate or spastic colons should whirl seeds in their coffee grinders and eat them with cereal or during an apple juice fast. Take some castor oil to speed up the elimination process.

One of the little-known symptoms of parasites in the body is a tendency to have a florid coloring around the nose and cheek area. Other symptoms are itching, fluttering and spasms of the colon, bloating, flatulence, pain, irritability and increased hunger. Sometimes a person will dream of having "germs" or unwanted objects in their bodies. All too often the digestive tract is ignored by physicians, yet it contains hundreds of different types of parasites: worms and amoebas ranging in size from thoses too small to be seen without a microscope to a tape worm which can grow many feet longer than the human body it inhabits; it is a creature rivaling any Hollywood horror movie! Disbelievers with strong stomachs can use a jeweler's magnifying glass or a microscope to examine suspicious contents expelled from their colon during a fast.

When parasites invade vital organs or other parts of the body, strange symptoms can manifest. Standard medical tests may be diagnostically ineffective. If you suspect the problem, try to find a medical specialist who knows the proper test to give for detection. Routine fecal or urine samples may not find anything because the sample may be clean.

An interesting phenomenon noted by people trying to improve their "spiritual vibrations" is that the body will "dump" unwanted contents as the person has the proper intent and begins following some of the procedures described in this book. Mind and body do work together to change cellular structure. From a physical standpoint, vermin prefer unhealthy, more easily invaded environments in much the same way that cockroaches like trashy living arrangements and fleas like weak dogs. Once a person begins to improve his health, stronger body tissue results and the pests find it harder to find a disease pocket in which to take up residence.

Anyone beginning a new health technique should begin slowly, use moderation, and continue until the desired results are achieved. Don't give up and abandon your good efforts; your persistence will pay off!

# 7 From Earth to Moon

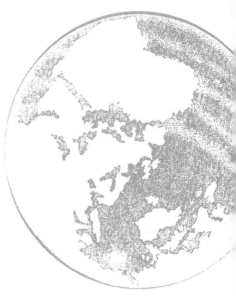

> In our every deliberation, we must consider the impact of our decisions on the next seven generations.
> —FROM THE GREAT LAW OF THE IROQUOIS CONFEDERACY

Our forefathers used ideas from the Iroquois Federation when they wrote our Declaration of Independence. Today in an effort toward better personal health and the preservation of our planet, we again seek ancient wisdom. Spiritual and natural healing methods make us eager to blend native ways with new technologies. It is helpful to compare the thought patterns of traditional red Mmen to those of the European colonists if we are to have success combining the old and new ways toward a better future for all.

## Traditional Thinking

RED MAN
Holistic healing
Earth is sacred

WHITE MAN
Treating symptoms
Earth is to use

| RED MAN | WHITE MAN |
| --- | --- |
| Time is circular | Time is linear |
| Time is relative | Time is precise |
| Community thinking | Individual thinking |
| Questioning intrusive | Questioning necessary |
| Spiritual | Religious |
| Ambition is crass | Ambition admired |
| Advice ill-mannered | Advice is to be given |
| Earth/creatures sacred | Earth/creatures relative |
| Children are little adults | Children need guidance |
| Life is teacher | Authorities teach |
| Staring rude | Staring shows interest |
| Honor above winning | Winning brings honor |
| Person valued | Accomplishment valued |
| Today-oriented | Goal-oriented |
| Creative ideas within | Creative ideas external |
| Kinesthetic learner | Visual/or direct learner |
| Talking depletes energy | Talking gets things done |
| Actions show character | Actions bring success |
| Power is an energy | Power is control |
| Possessions communal | Possessions owned |

Tradition changes and every person is an individual with his own set of values. Today's Americans are a mixture of races, ideas, religions and goals. The strength of all Americans and people around the world lies in their diversity and ability to change as needed. The traditional views, as described above, reflect the Eastern and Western cultures of the world. While few people today can claim a "full-blood" heritage, meaning ancestors from only one genetic pool or country, Native Americans' DNA is Oriental in origin, since Native Americans crossed over the Bering Strait into the Americas. The Caucasian DNA originated in Western Europe.

Only the strongest Native Americans survived the European invasion. Only the hardiest, most aggressive Caucasians, blacks and Orientals survived to arrive in the Americas. As a group, they form the American prototype known the world over as ambitious, aggressive, intelligent, capable, attractive, emotional and, yes, crass and "uncultured." Survival of our planet demands that we retain the best traditional and contemporary ideas, and dismiss those that are truly outdated or destructive. By combining Eastern introspection and Western action it is possible to heal ourselves, others, and the planet. We start with our own health, branch out (in our own way) to help those less fortunate, and then think globally.

## Natural Plants and Products to Heal

1. Eat whole natural foods and you won't need healing.
2. Eat foods your ancestors ate that are also an appropriate fit to your body type and digestive system.
3. Use herbs for healing and you'll stay healthier.
4. Save modern medicines for emergency needs.
5. Cultivate an appreciation and reverence for all living things, including our earth.
6. Whenever possible, eliminate the use of herbicides, insecticides and strong chemicals in your home.
7. Patronize companies that specialize in herbal ingredients and that avoid animal testing.
8. Join an organization that benefits the children or vegetation of our planet (both young, growing things).

### HEALING FOODS AND HERBS

*Heart:* To heal the physical heart use hawthorn berry, capsicum and wood betony herbs, and take lecithin, raw wheat germ, vitamin E, black-strap molasses, cod liver oil and brewer's yeast supplements. Garlic, foods with potassium like bananas and oranges, along with kidney herbs, help to reduce blood pressure.

To heal the emotional heart, use flower essences and essential oils such as rose, jasmine, and lilac. Use incense or take tinctures. Sniff flowers or essences in one nostril and exhale from the other. Reverse sides. Seek love by loving yourself first and then giving love.

*Kidney:* To help the kidney use juniper berry, dandelion, parsley, uva ursa, corn silk and yarrow, and eat asparagus, cranberries and green vegetables. Take liquid chlorophyll and use apple cider vinegar and lemon juice in recipes and drinks. Fresh asparagus and melons rank the highest for beneficial effects. Watermelon meals, in place of any other food, especially at night, give the kidneys a rest.

Don't hold in feelings, as the kidneys stores old fear and facilitate repression. Combat fear. Talking therapy helps release unconscious old memories and suppressions.

*Adrenals:* For herbs to aid the adrenal glands, see the power herbs listed in chapter one. Of them, licorice is the best healer, while the others increase individual energy.

The adrenals, which sit above the kidney, control the "fight or flight" reaction that is a survival instinct. Regaining personal power over one's life greatly enhances the adrenals, as the need to fight for control is greatly diminished.

*Liver/Gall Bladder:* Take the herbs yellow dock, dandelion, parsley, barberry, and Oregon grape root. Use colon-cleansing herbs. Brewer's yeast (contains essential minerals), vitamin C, vitamins A and D in oil form and lecithin supplements are also helpful. Tomatoes, or tomato juice, and mixed tomato/vegetable juices are excellent, probably the best food for liver cleansing as they stimulate bile production. Fresh red beets, radishes and raspberries are also good.

Emotionally, the liver and gall bladder store up anger and keep old grudges. Emotional release of anger and consequent forgiving needs to be accomplished for optimum health of these organs.

*Brain and Nervous System:* Nervines are listed in chapter four. To those mentioned, add chamomile, wild yam, lobelia and passionflower to teas to help calm nerves. Gota kola, ginkgo, regular tea and coffee, and DMAE-H3, a supplement, increase mental acuity and memory. Calcium and alkaline food (sweet fruits, vegetables, legumes) and cod liver oil keep the acid balance in check, aiding nerves. Lecithin and vitamin E are essential for brain health. Whole cereal (with the germ), as well as sunflower and pumpkin seeds, contains lecithin and vitamin E. Brewer's yeast, valuable for minerals, and the B vitamin complex complete the nerve foods.

For emotional health, be true to yourself and follow the road that allows you to do the things that are appropriate, rewarding and relevant to you as a unique individual.

*Lungs:* Ginger, cinnamon, eucalyptus, capsicum, and lobelia mixed with mullein, Saint John's-wort, raspberry and ephedra are helpful herbs in food, tea or capsule form. Okra, comfrey, marshmallow and slippery elm help soothe mucous membranes. Cranberries, whole citrus fruits with pulp, lemon juice, onions, hot peppers, garlic, blackberries and raspberries are foods which help clear the bronchial tubes.

Asthma and bronchial congestion are sometimes an unconscious plea for love and help. Take whatever means possible to unlock these love blocks in your life and to become aware of your own needs and what you do to prevent those needs from being filled.

*Pancreas:* More than any other organ, the status of the pancreas seems to be a highly individualistic matter, probably based on a combination of genetic constitution and one's eccentric personality. Pancreatic status appears also to be a result of hormonal and enzymatic functioning and interactions. Digestive enzymes containing pancreatin seem to be helpful to people over the age of forty. Juniper berries, licorice, wild yam, golden seal, uva ursa, and astragalus may be useful. The latter is a naturally sweet herbal sugar. Dong quai, devil's club, and hamula-prodigiosa herbs may be helpful. In place of white sugar, black-strap molasses, maple sugar and honey deliver valuable nutrients. Fresh sunchokes or Jerusalem artichokes are healing to the pancreas as no insulin is present until the tuber is older. Diabetics must consult their physicians before assuming new dietary practices.

The pancreas is a finely tuned organ easily upset by excesses. Heavy smoking and too much caffeine, cola, tea, coffee or alcohol consumption is hard on the pancreas. Of all the cancers, pancreatic cancer is the most deadly and the quickest.

Try to live a well-balanced life in moderation. It is the writer's opinion that problems in the pancreas reflect a lack of flow between the vital chakras of the body—spiritual, emotional, and sexual. In Native American terms: a soul problem.

*Sexual Organs:* Dong quay for women, Siberian ginseng for men, damiana and kava kava for both sexes. Raspberries are cleansing along with citrus fruits. The nerve herbs listed in chapter four are helpful. While pumpkin seeds are especially beneficial to the sexual organs, wheat germ, oatmeal, whole-grain cornmeal, organic cereals and any nut (peanuts, filbert, pecans, black walnuts, soy beans, sunflower seeds, sesame seeds) are recommended. Take vitamin E and wheat-germ oil supplements daily for increased sexual efficiency. For sexual problems not helped with herbs and nutrition, look first for two problems: diabetes and heavy smoking of standard cigarettes (which contain salt peter).

Once these possibilities are eliminated we must then mention the most frequent cause of sexual problems—relationship problems:

1. An unsatisfactory relationship where there is a lack of love or trust.
2. Not being in a relationship because of avoiding contact with the opposite sex or choosing partners incapable of intimacy.

In either case, look to yourself, determine what kind of a partner you need and take the actions needed to change your life and yourself.

*Stomach, Small Intestines and Colon:* Chapter six deals extensively with these digestive organs. They are crucial to overall good health because a lack of proper absorption from a healthy colon prevents good nutrients being absorbed and used by the body.

*Best Supplements:* For health's sake, when you can't or don't want to take the time to eat the proper foods, use the following supplements every day if possible: Kelp or dulse tablets, wheat germ (dump on cold cereal), vitamin A, B complex, vitamin C with bioflavoids, vitamin E, lecithin, multi-mineral tablet, digestive enzymes after a meal—drink the juice drink daily (described in detail in chapter six, adding one tablespoon of brewer's yeast to the drink). Whenever possible eat vegetables and drink one V8 or tomato juice or have salsa daily. Avoid white sugar, white yeast breads, soft-drinks, candy and snack foods such as chips. Eat an apple and orange when possible. Keep sunflower and pumpkin seeds (pipitas) with you to snack on along with dried figs and prunes. On the weekends, experiment with eating foods suggested in this book. Good luck and remember—you are what you eat and what you think!

# Beauty Health Products

### HERBAL FACIAL AND BODY SKIN NATURAL PRODUCTS

The winning all-around, organic– and non-animal testing company combined with great products is Aubrey Organics, located in Tampa, Florida. Don't miss their Sea Ware facial cleanser, Sun Protection Herbal Butter and Apricot Midroxy with natural fruit acids. Great for men's skin too.

### HERBAL COSMETICS AND HAIR PRODUCTS

Write Aveda Corporation in Minneapolis, Minnesota. Products for men as well as women. They have their own stores in malls and sell through beauty shops as well. They carry a hair spray that is propelled with air, not the harmful hydrocarbons that destroy the ozone layer.

Rachel Perry is a natural cosmetic line of lipsticks and eye shadow, as well as foundations and cremes, that is sold in health-food stores.

### COMMERCIAL COSMETICS WITH ADDED HERBALS

Adrian Arpel Cosmetics are sold on the Internet and have a history of researching natural ingredients for makeup foundation. Check labels as products vary. Best bet: Glycerin Liquid Powder, the liquid foundation with the fewest added chemicals.

Clarins, from Paris, France, is an international cosmetic line that has always incorporated herbal formulas in its ingredients. Read the labels.

St. Ives, a new, inexpensive Swiss line of skin product contains herbs. It is sold in grocery stores and drugstores and consists primarily of facial and skin cleansers and moisturizers.

If you have your own plants, slice off a piece (no more than what you will use that day) and use it as a moisturizer. It soothes chapped and irritated skin and is good for sunburns. TwinLab makes an aloe vera Na-PCA spray that combines the aloe gel with the natural sodium found in the skin. Naturade and Nature's Life brands both provide aloe vera gel products that are excellent. If you want to stay looking young, use the spray and then an aloe gel in the morning before shaving or applying makeup.

Now Foods of Glendale Heights, Illinois, makes a natural glycerin product that can be used internally or externally. Mix one drop with your usual products for increased moisture protection for your skin, or add one-half teaspoon to your health drink.

Edgar Cayce, the famous psychic healer, recommended products for better health. The Heritage Store, in Virginia Beach, will send you a catalog that is full of wonderful, hard-to-find health items, true to the originals recommended by Cayce, and more.

## For Your Home and Health

*Glass Cleaner:* Use an empty commercial glass cleaner spray bottle filled with equal parts of white vinegar and water.

*Cleanser:* Bon Ami is the safest.

*Detergent:* Seventh Generation Brand, Broomfield, Colorado, use only recycled paper. Order your paper products—toilet tissue, kleenex, paper towels—bulk from them, postage free, and quit having to shop so often. Recycled paper saves our trees.

*Dishwasher Detergent:* Lifetree automatic dishwasher liquid. You only use a teaspoon; it lasts a long time.

*Burned Pans:* Dump salt to cover burned places, then cover

with white vinegar. Let sit twenty-four hours. Scrub out with brush. Repeat if necessary.

*Insect Control:* Order environmental garden supplies from Gardens Alive.

*Lawn Control:* Depending on your climate, think about having cactus or wild flowers as part of your lawn. Use plants for groundcover wherever possible. If you use compost on your lawn to build the health of your grass, you won't need herbicides. Grow edible plants and herbs in your yard and garden.

*Edible Plants and Useful Herbs:* Lobelia, echinacea, yarrow, sage, pennyroyal, catnip, valerian, garlic, onion, mustard, sunflowers, juniper, nasturtiums, aloe vera, rose, ginseng, licorice, Saint John's-wort, parsley, lily of the valley, poke, lamb's-quarter, chives, witch hazel are among the many herbs and plants you can grow easily and enjoy. *The Complete Book of Edible Landscaping,* by Rosalind Creasy and published by the Sierra Club, is appropriate for homes in a variety of different climates.

*Garden Vegetables:* Think about growing your own vegetables. Instead of putting vegetable and fruit garbage down the disposal, put it in a compost pile. If you aren't interested in growing, but want to eat organically, order a catalog from The Walnut Acres, a fifty-year-old organic farm in Pennsylvania.

*Plants and Herbs in the Wild:* If you are a hiker or outdoors person and want to eat wild plants, be sure you know what you're picking. Read up before you attempt trial-and-error identification and avoid any plants with poisonous look-a-likes. The book *Wild Edibles of Missouri,* published by the Missouri Department of Conservation, was written by Jan Phillips, who has tried recipes and gives you the results. In your own community, check bulletin boards for naturalistic groups offering courses in herb location and survival in the wild.

*Green Supplements:* If you don't eat green plants and herbs, help your health by taking liquid chlorophyll or a green supplement like Kyo-Green everyday. Or try alfalfa greens, barley greens, spiralini or other green products.

## Help the Planet

Join a group interested in the welfare of your community or world. The Sierra Club attempts to watch harmful legislation affecting our forests (yes it is still happening). It has chapters in every large city.

Greenpeace, Save the Children, and rain forest organizations generally have 800 numbers so there is no charge to call any of them for membership information.

Note: All brands, groups, addresses and the quality of products are subject to change with new ownership, corporate mergers or changes of directors. Please assess all recommendations yourself and compare to similar products. New health supplements will appear as discoveries are made, and, one hopes, present better-quality items. In keeping with the nature of this chapter, please make your own judgments, and keep the best of the old ways and add new methods.

# Notes

1 Lewis Henry Morgan, *The Indian Journals 1859–62*, University of Michigan, 1959
2 Ibid
3 Dr. Benjamin Barton, "Collections for an Essay Towards s Materia Medica of the United States," as researched by Virgil J. Vogel, *American Indian Medicine*, University of Oklahoma Press, 1970
4 *Journal of a Voyage to North America*, Ed. Louise Phelps Kellogg, reported by Virgil Vogel in *American Indian Medicine*
5 John Lawson, *A New Voyage to South Carolina*, Chapel Hill, 1967
6 Joseph Epes Brown is interpreting the meaning of terms used by the White Buffalo Maiden told to him by Black Elk and written in Brown's book *The Sacred Pipe*, University of Oklahoma Press, 1953
7 A Lakota Indian quoted in *Pipe, Bible and Peyote Among the Oglala Lakota*, by Stein, Metz, and Alquist, Stockholm
8 Joseph Epes Brown as interpreting the meaning of terms used by the White Buffalo Maiden told to him by Black Elk and written in Brown's book *The Sacred Pipe*, University of Oklahoma Press, 1953
9 Translated by Paul Radin, in "Autobiography of Winnebago Indian," University of California Publications in *American Archeology and Ethnology*, Vol. 17, #7, 1920
10 Research by Robert M. Uteley author of *The Lance and The Shield: The Life and Times of Sitting Bull*, Henry Holt, N.Y., 1993
11 Ibid
12 Ibid
13 Bird and animal interpretation in *Native American Magic and Medicine* by Mary Atwood, Sterling Publishing, NY 1991
14 Harold Driver, *Indians of North America*, University of Chicago Press, 1961
15 Jack Henningfield of the National Institute of Drug Abuse in *Brain/Mind Bulletin*, 1986.

[16] Hawkins, in "A Sketch of the Creek Country," reported by James Howard in *Oklahoma Seminoles*, University of Oklahoma Press, 1984

[17] Lewis Henry Morgan, *The Indian Journals 1859–62*, University of Michigan, 1959

[18] Donald M. Bahr, "Pima and Papago Medicine and Philosophy" in *Handbook For North American Indians*, Great Basin Volume XI, Smithsonian Institute, 1979

[19] Richard Lucas, *Common & Uncommon uses of Herbs for Healthful Living*, Arco, 1982

[20] Mary Atwood, *Native American Magic and Medicine* by Mary Atwood, Sterling Publishing, NY 1991 (describes how to do a vision quest)

[21] Melvin Gilmore, *Uses of Plants by the Indians of the Missouri River Region*, University of Nebraska Press, 1977.

[22] Small section of the vision by Black Elk in 1932 written in *Black Elk Speaks* by John Neihardt

[23] John Heinerman, author of *Science of Herbal Medicine*, BiWorld Publishers: Orem, Utah, 1984

[24] Paul B. Hamel & Mary U. Chiltoskey, authors of *Cherokee Plants, their uses—a 400 year history*. Library of Congress Catalog Card Number 75-27776

[25] Melvin Gilmore, *Uses of Plants by the Indians of the Missouri River Region*, University of Nebraska Press, 1977.

[26] Alma Hutchens, *Indian Herbalogy of North America*, Shambhala, Boston, 1973

[27] Humbert Santillo, N.D. author of *Natural Healing with Herbs*, Hohm Press, Prescott, AZ 1993

[28] Jon Manchip White, *Everyday Life of the North American Indian*, Dorsett Press, NY 1979

[29] Gene Weltfish, *The Lost Universe: Pawnee Life and Culture*, Nebraska Press, 1977

[30] Harold Driver, *Indians of North America*, University of Chicago Press, 1961

[31] Ibid

[32] John Heinerman, author of *Science of Herbal Medicine*, BiWorld Publishers: Orem, Utah, 1984

[33] Vaughn M. Bryant, Jr., "The Role of Coprolite Analysis in Archeology;" *Bulletin of the Texas Archaeological Society*, Vol. 45, 1974

[34] Harold Driver, *Indians of North America*, University of Chicago Press, 1961

[35] Michael Weiner, *Earth Medicine Earth Food*, Ballantine Books, 1972

[36] John Heinerman, author of *Science of Herbal Medicine*, BiWorld Publishers: Orem, Utah, 1984

[37] Virgil J. Vogel, *American Indian Medicine*, University of Oklahoma Press, 1970

# Index

# About the Author

Mary Dean Atwood, Ph.D., is a contemporary medicine woman from Oklahoma. She has a doctorate in clinical psychology from the University of New Mexico. Natural nutritional healing is a lifelong personal interest which she has researched extensively. She has a devotion to the welfare of animals and children and is also dedicated to preserving nature's plants and trees. She currently resides in Arizona.